BASIC differential equa

To Moya and Chad and to Peggy, Michael and Katharine

BASIC differential equations

J C Mason, MA, DPhil, FIMA

Professor and Head
Computational Mathematics Group
Royal Military College of Science
Shrivenham
Swindon
Wilts

D C Stocks, DipTech, MSc, FIMA

Senior Lecturer and Acting Head
Mathematics and Ballistics Group
Royal Military College of Science
Shrivenham
Swindon
Wilts

Butterworths
London . Boston . Durban . Singapore . Sydney . Toronto . Wellington

First published 1987

© **Butterworth & Co. (Publishers) Ltd, 1987**

British Library Cataloguing in Publication Data

Mason, J.C.
  BASIC differential equations.
  1. Differential equations—Data
  processing   2.   BASIC (Computer program
  language)
  I. Title   II.   Stocks, D.C.
  515.3′5′02855133   QA371

  ISBN 0–408–01520–9

Library of Congress Cataloging-in-Publication Data

Mason, J. C.
  BASIC differential equations.
  Includes bibliographies and index.
  1. Differential equations—Numerical solutions.
  2. Differential equations—Numerical solutions—Data
  processing.   3.   BASIC (Computer program language)
  I. Stocks, D. C.   II.   Title.
  QA372.M384   1987   515.3′5   86–31780

  ISBN 0–408–01520–9

Typeset by August Filmsetting, Haydock, St. Helens, Lancs.
Printed and bound in England by Page Bros Ltd., Norwich, Norfolk

Preface

Differential equations occur extremely frequently in the mathematical modelling of science and engineering problems. Indeed, it has been claimed that they occur in 80 per cent of all practical mathematical problems. Whether or not such a quantitative assessment is justifiable, there is little doubt about their qualitative importance.

This text concentrates on ordinary differential equations and does not cover partial differential equations. Moreover, it is primarily, though not entirely, concerned with numerical methods of solution. Such methods may lead to systems of linear algebraic equations, which have to be solved by matrix methods. There is therefore a strong link between the subject matter of the present book and that of our preceding volumes on *BASIC Numerical Mathematics* and *BASIC Matrix Methods*. The three texts together cover the most fundamental topics in numerical mathematical modelling.

Like its two predecessors, the present book is geared to the requirements of undergraduate engineers in the overall spirit of the books in the Butterworths BASIC series. However, it should also meet the needs of a wide range of engineers, mathematicians and scientists who wish to solve practical problems involving differential equations on a computer. It should be particularly useful as a text for mathematics and numerical mathematics courses, engineering problems courses, and computer applications courses.

That this book covers an important subject is not sufficient justification on its own. However, we believe that there are three aspects of the book which deserve special attention. First, it follows the philosophy of all the books in the BASIC series, in providing engineers with a good selection of well-documented BASIC computer programs for carrying out a variety of key methods on a range of standard problems. Secondly, it follows an apparently novel approach in presenting BASIC programs not only for general numerical methods, but also for fundamental analytical methods. Thus it covers some of the material normally given only in traditional mathematical texts as well as including the more conventional numerical mathematical material. Thirdly, the book attempts to give a straightforward but fairly detailed exposition of the theoretical background to the methods, suitable to practising scientists and engineers.

The traditional mathematical material (in Chapter 4) referred to above is primarily concerned with the auxiliary equation method for determining complementary functions and the D operator method for finding particular integrals. The BASIC programs for these methods consist mainly of logical decisions about which types of solutions occur, depending for example on the nature of the zeros of the auxiliary equation, rather than on arithmetic or numerical calculations. In contrast, the numerical mathematical material (in Chapters 3, 5 and 6) provides the techniques for solving general problems, and the BASIC programs for such methods are primarily concerned with calculations.

As in the earlier texts, we have aimed to strike the right balance between numerical methods and numerical analysis, both of which are necessary for engineers. Although we have not always been able to cover the most powerful methods which would be used in practice (such as variable step–variable order methods based on error control), we have nevertheless been able to cover the key types of method (such as the Runge–Kutta and Adams methods) and analyse their stability.

A significant number of problems are posed at the end of chapters, including a wide variety of engineering problems. There are, roughly speaking, three types of problem: those that aid and test understanding of the chapter contents, those that give practice with programs, and those that extend programs.

Readers who wish to look up programs in the book are referred to the contents list for page references. The programs themselves are placed within the body of the text rather than in a separate section. They are generally preceded by algorithms which summarize the logical steps, and followed by sample runs which demonstrate the program's performance and by program notes which give additional information.

The style of our BASIC programming is similar to that of our earlier books, though we make more use here of subroutines (by way of the GOSUB and RETURN statements), especially in Chapter 4. All programs are interactive with input and output of all information at the keyboard. Readers who require batch-mode programs, which include their own data, may readily modify the programs in the book by using READ and DATA statements in place of INPUT statements (see Chapter 1).

The actual contents of the book consist of three short introductory chapters followed by three substantial chapters on major topics. Chapters 1 to 3 give introductions to the three key aspects of the book: the BASIC computer language, differential equations, and numerical mathematics and finite differences.

Chapter 4 covers analytical methods for determining solutions to some important but fundamental linear problems, for which numerical methods are not needed. In contrast, Chapter 5 looks at numerical methods for solving general initial-value problems for differential equations, which may be non-linear, starting with elementary Euler–trapezium methods and progressing to higher order Runge–Kutta methods and predictor–corrector methods.

Chapter 6 then turns to numerical methods for boundary-value problems, concentrating on linear second order equations. Here the emphasis is on finite-difference models leading to the solution of linear algebraic equations, and a variety of types of boundary conditions are discussed. Beam bending problems provide simple but useful examples for the introduction of methods.

The book is primarily intended for undergraduate use by engineers, scientists and mathematicians. However, it would also be useful as introductory material for graduates who are unfamiliar with numerical techniques.

We are grateful to colleagues at the Royal Military College of Science at Shrivenham for helping with this book in a variety of ways. In particular we are indebted to Mrs Pamela Moore for preparing the manuscript with great patience and precision.

J.C.M.
D.C.S.

Contents

Chapter 1

Introduction to BASIC

1.1 Computer programs and programming languages

A computer program is a set of instructions which a computer is able to interpret and execute. These instructions are designed to perform a particular task, and in our case this task is to determine the numerical solution of a differential equation. In order that the instructions may be recognized, they must be written in a standard programming language (such as BASIC, FORTRAN, ALGOL, PASCAL, COBOL, etc.) for which an interpreter or compiler is available on the computer. The interpreter transforms each instruction in the programming language into a set of fundamental instructions in a machine language, designed to be simple and instantly recognizable to the computer. The programming language is designed to be convenient and practicable for the user, and BASIC is one such programming language.

1.2 The BASIC approach—advantages and disadvantages

All of the programs in this book are written in BASIC. While BASIC was originally intended for use on time-sharing computer systems, it has now gained widespread popularity as the main language associated with microcomputers. The main advantages of BASIC are that it is easy to learn, convenient to use, and particularly well suited to conversational programming in which the user interacts with the computer throughout the running of the program.

The simple version of BASIC used in this book has a number of disadvantages, and these mainly concern its lack of structure in comparison with languages like FORTRAN or PASCAL. For example, it is not usual in BASIC to distinguish between integers and other numbers, to have variables of double length (for more accurate calculations), or to use one program as a subroutine or subprogram for another program. Moreover, BASIC has a particular disadvantage in numerical analysis, which relates to its apparently commendable feature of rounding to integer values any numbers that are very close

1

to integers. This makes it difficult to test the conditioning of any problem that has integer data, and inadvisable to use integer data as test data in gauging the rounding error in any program.

This book is not intended as an instruction manual in BASIC. For that purpose the reader is referred to the references at the end of the chapter or to one of many similar works. One of our aims, however, is to help the student learn BASIC by applying it to solve mathematical problems, especially those that occur in science and engineering. This aim can be met by the reader if he studies and tests the programs in the book, and also tries to write his own programs based on some of the problems given at the ends of the chapters. Although the book does not give every detail of the grammar of BASIC, a description of the main features of BASIC is given below.

1.3 The elements of BASIC

1.3.1 Program structure and sequencing

A BASIC program is a sequence of statements which define a procedure for the computer to follow (rather like a cooking recipe for a chef to follow). As it follows this procedure, the computer allocates values to each of the variables encountered and changes them where instructed. Statements used in the program are of a number of types, which will be discussed in more detail in following sections. They include REM statements (for making program notes), DIM statements (for allocating subscripted variables), INPUT or READ statements (for defining data), assignment statements (for doing mathematics), conditional statements (for controlling the action of the program) and PRINT statements (for printing out results).

Every statement must be preceded by a line number. On running the program, all statements are executed in the sequence that corresponds to these line numbers. For example, the program

```
100 X = 1             is executed as  100 X = 1
400 GO TO 200                         200 X = X + 1
300 PRINT X                           300 PRINT X
200 X = X + 1                         400 GO TO 200
```

The use of numbering greatly simplifies correcting and editing (see Section 2.5).

1.3.2 Mathematical expressions

In mathematics it is necessary to evaluate expressions which involve numerical constants, variables (e.g. x), and functions (e.g. sin). All constants are treated identically in BASIC, whether they are integer (e.g. 36) or real (e.g. 36.1). They may be entered in either fixed point form (e.g. 36.1) or floating point form (e.g. 0.361 E2), although the computer prints out numbers in fixed point form unless they are small or large. The constant π is often available by typing PI or the π key.

Variables, which fulfil the role of letters in algebra, may be named by any one of the letters A to Z, or by any letter followed by a digit (e.g. A3, P7, etc.). Each variable is allocated a location in the computer store, and it takes the numerical value recorded in that location. This numerical value is substituted for the corresponding variable whenever that variable occurs in an expression, and so it is important to ensure that the correct value is given to a variable initially.

The function square root may be evaluated via the built-in computer function SQR, $\sqrt{x}$ being replaced by SQR(X). The argument in brackets (X) may be any number, variable, or mathematical expression. Other built-in functions include SIN(X), COS(X), LOG(X), EXP(X), ABS(X) and INT(X) which represent, respectively, sin x, cos x, ln x (i.e. $\log_e x$), $|x|$, and the integer part of x. For trigonometric functions (SIN, etc.) the argument is assumed to be measured in radians.

Mathematical expressions are formed from constants, variables and functions by inserting arithmetic operations such as plus, times, etc. These operations have a hierarchy, which determines the order in which they are performed by the computer, and it is as follows:

to the power of (^)
multiply (*) and divide (/)
add (+) and subtract (−)

If two or more operations have the same hierarchy, then the computer works from left to right. Brackets always take precedence and should be used to provide clarity and avoid ambiguity. The first left bracket is paired with the last right bracket, and so on. Hence

$$\frac{a+b}{3c}$$

becomes either

(A + B)/(3*C) or (A + B)/3/C

Some examples of correct and incorrect BASIC expressions are as follows:

Mathematical Expression	Correct BASIC	Incorrect BASIC
$x \sin x$	X * SIN(X)	X SIN(X)
$\dfrac{1-r^n}{1-r}$	(1 − R^N)/(1 − R)	1 − R^N/1 − R
$\ln(1+\sqrt{x})$	LOG(1 + SQR(X))	LOG(1 + SQR(X)
$\left\| \dfrac{1+\sin x}{x} \right\|$	ABS((1 + SIN(X))/X)	ABS(1 + SIN(X))/X

1.3.3 Assignment statements

An assignment statement takes the form

line number [LET] variable = mathematical expression

The word LET here is usually optional, and will be omitted throughout this book. (Square brackets are used in this chapter to indicate optional items.) For example, a root of a quadratic equation

$$x_1 = (-b + \sqrt{b^2 - 4ac})/(2a)$$

may be obtained by a statement such as

100 X1 = (− B + SQR(B^2 − 4*A*C))/(2*A)

It is important, however, to realize that an assignment statement is not itself an equation. It is an instruction to give the variable on the left-hand side the numerical value of the expression on the right-hand side. Thus we may have a statement such as

50 X = X + 1

which increases by 1 the value of X.

There is no mathematical statement in common usage which is precisely equivalent to the assignment statement

X = Y

However, in this book we shall use the symbol ': =' to denote 'becomes', so that the precisely equivalent mathematical statement is

$$x := y$$

(The symbol ': =' is used in place of ' =' for assignment statements in the ALGOL language.)

1.3.4 Input

In *conversational programming* the user specifies values of variables by INPUT statements at 'run-time'. The statement has the form

line number INPUT variable 1 [, variable 2, . . .]

e.g.

20 INPUT A, B, C

When the program is run the computer prints ? on reaching this statement, and waits for the user to type values for the variables, e.g. ? 5, 10, 15 which are interpreted as $A = 5$, $B = 10$, $C = 15$ in the above example.

An alternative form of data input is used if there are many data, or if the data are unlikely ever to be changed, or if the user does not want to converse with the computer. In this case a statement of the form

line number READ variable 1 [, variable 2, . . .]

e.g.

20 READ A, B, C   (1.1)

is used in conjunction with a statement (or number of statements) of the form

line number DATA number 1 [, number 2, . . .]

e.g. either

21 DATA 5, 10, 15   (1.2)

or

$$\left.\begin{array}{l} 21 \text{ DATA } 5 \\ 22 \text{ DATA } 10 \\ 23 \text{ DATA } 15 \end{array}\right\}\tag{1.3}$$

On executing a READ statement, values are assigned to variables from the DATA statements in the order in which the latter occur in the program. If (1.1) is followed by either (1.2) or (1.3), then A, B and C are allocated values 5, 10 and 15.

1.3.5 Output

The output of data (for checking purposes) and the results of calculations etc. is done by a statement of form

line number PRINT list

where the list may contain variables or expressions
e.g.

200 PRINT A, B, C, A*B/C

or text enclosed in quotes
e.g.

10 PRINT "VALUES OF A, B, C:";

or a mixture of both
e.g.

300 PRINT "X = "; X, "Y = "; Y

The items in the list are separated by commas or semi-colons. Commas ensure a tabulation in columns about 15 spaces wide, while a semi-colon suppresses such spacing. If a semi-colon is placed at the end of a list, it suppresses the line feed. If the list is left blank then a blank line is printed, and this is a useful way of spacing out results.

Note the necessity to use PRINT statements to copy out all numbers which are input by INPUT or READ/DATA statements, so that there is a true record of them. PRINT statements should also precede INPUT statements for explanatory purposes, since ? on its own is not informative. For example, the pair of statements

10 PRINT "WHAT IS X";
20 INPUT X

leads to the computer output

WHAT IS X?

in reply to which the value of X is typed in.

1.3.6 Conditional statements

It is often necessary to take a course of action if, and only if, some condition is fulfilled. This is done with a statement of the form

line number IF expression 1 $\underset{\text{operator}}{\overset{\text{conditional}}{}}$ expression 2 THEN line number

where the possible 'conditional operators' are

=   equals
< > not equal to
<   less than
< = less than or equal to
>   greater than
> = greater than or equal to

For example, a program could contain the following statements if it is to stop when a zero value of N is input.

$$
\left.
\begin{array}{l}
20 \text{ INPUT N} \\
30 \text{ IF N} <> 0 \text{ THEN } 50 \\
40 \text{ STOP} \\
50 \ldots
\end{array}
\right\}
\qquad (1.4)
$$

Note the statement STOP which ends the physical run of a program. This is not to be confused with the statement END which is the (optional) last statement occurring in the program listing.

We might point out here that some modern implementations of BASIC permit the use of IF ... THEN ... ELSE statements. Such statements can greatly enhance the tidiness and structured nature of a program by avoiding overuse of GO TO statements (see below), and so their use should be encouraged. For example, if your system allows it, the single statement

10 IF $X = 0$ THEN $E = 1$ ELSE $E = (X - Y)/X$

is equivalent to the more conventional but less tidy piece of code

10 IF $X = 0$ THEN 40
20 $E = (X - Y)/X$
30 GO TO 50
40 $E = 1$
50 ...

1.3.7 Loops

There are several ways in which a program may be made to repeat part of its procedure, and the simplest is to use the statement.

line number GO TO line number

For example, if the statement

60 GO TO 20

is added to the instructions (1.4), then the program will execute statement 50 for a sequence of input values of N until a zero is input.

The most common way of doing loops is to start with a 'FOR statement'

line number FOR variable = expression 1 TO expression 2 [STEP expression 3]

where the STEP is assumed to be unity if it is omitted, and to end the loop with

line number NEXT variable

The same variable is used in both FOR and NEXT statements, and its value should not be changed in the intervening statements.

A loop is used if, for example, N sets of data X, Y have to be read and a mathematical expression such as sin(X + Y) calculated in each case.

e.g.

```
10 READ N
20 PRINT "X", "Y", "SIN(X + Y)"
30 FOR I = 1 TO N
40 READ X,Y
50 PRINT X, Y, SIN(X + Y)
60 NEXT I
```

Loops may also be used to calculate sums and products of a list of expressions, and this is discussed in the following chapter in connection with the symbols Σ and Π.

1.3.8 Subscripted variables

It is frequently desirable in mathematics to use a variable with a subscript, such as x_i, so that many cases can be covered by a simple formula. For example, we might write

$$x_i = i^2 \quad (i = 1, 2, 3, \ldots, 10) \tag{1.5}$$

to specify that the xs are the squares of the integers up to 10 ($x_1 = 1$, $x_2 = 4$, $x_3 = 9$, ..., $x_{10} = 100$). In a BASIC program x_i is represented by X(I), the subscript being placed in brackets, and a specific numerical value must be assigned to I in the program, perhaps by a FOR loop. For example, (1.5) may be calculated from

```
10 FOR I = 1 TO 10
20 X(I) = I^2
30 NEXT I
```

It is also permitted for a variable to have two or more subscripts attached to it. For example, a matrix element a_{ij} may be represented by A(I,J).

Since a subscripted variable has more than one value associated with it (while a non-subscripted variable has just one), it is necessary to provide computer storage space for as many values as might be needed. This is done by a 'dimension statement' of the form line number DIM variable 1 (integer 1) [, variable 2 (integer 2), ...]

e.g.

10 DIM X(50), Y(50), A(10,10)

which allows up to 51 values $X(0), ..., X(50)$, up to 51 values $Y(0), ...,$ $Y(50)$, and up to 121 values $A(0,0), ..., A(10,10)$. The DIM statement must occur before the first use of the subscripted variables.

In some computers it is possible to do 'dynamic dimensioning' with a statement like

20 DIM X(N), Y(N)

provided that N has been previously defined, and this form is useful for avoiding wasted storage space.

1.3.9 Subroutines

Sometimes it is necessary to use a certain sequence of statements more than once in a program, and, in order to avoid repeating these statements, it is sensible to use a subroutine for this sequence. The program then contains statements such as

line number GOSUB line number

which causes the program to transfer control to a set of instructions (the subroutine) which starts at the second line number. The subroutine must end with an instruction of the form

line number RETURN

and the program then returns control from the subroutine to the statement immediately after the GOSUB call.

It is normally sensible to place subroutines at the end of a program, to keep them separate from the main body of the program.

1.3.10 Other statements

(a) *REM statements* are used for explanatory comments or headings in the program listing, and have the form

line number REM comment

e.g.

10 REM – THIS PROGRAM SOLVES $Y' = F(X,Y)$, $Y(0) = 1$

Such statements are ignored when the program is run. In some computers comments may be included on the same line as other statements.

(b) *String variables* enable the use of non-numeric data (e.g. words) and may be used, for example, for reading a combination of numbers and words. They will not be used in this book.

(c) *Multiple branching* can be done with statements of the form

line number ON expression THEN line number 1 [, line number 2, ...,]

or

line number ON expression GOSUB line number 1 [, line number 2, ...,]

The program transfers to the line number 1, line number 2, ... according as the integer value of the expression is 1, 2, ...

(d) *Function definition statements* are important in mathematics since they enable us to define our own functions (in addition to built-in functions such as SIN(X)). New functions may have any of the names FNA, FNB, ..., FNZ and are created by a statement such as

$$100 \text{ DEF FNA(X)} = .5*(\text{EXP}(X) + \text{EXP}(-X)) \tag{1.6}$$

which forms the function $\cosh(x)$.

Any defined function, e.g. FNA(X) above, is simply used in the main body of the program in a statement such as

10 Y = FNA(1)

which sets Y equal to $\cosh(1)$ if FNA is defined by (1.6).

Many computers allow functions of several variables. Thus the function $f(x,y) = x^2 + y^2$ might be named in the program as FNF(X,Y) and defined by the statement

$$200 \text{ DEF FNF(X,Y)} = X^2 + Y^2$$

It is advisable to check the rules for the placement of DEF statements for your particular computer system. If the system permits it, then there is an advantage in placing such statements near the end of the program, since they are then easily referenced and modified in order to solve new problems. However, some systems require each DEF statement to be placed at a line number *before* the first use of the corresponding function FN ...; it is simplest in that case to place all DEF statements at the beginning of the program along with DIM statements.

1.4 Matrix routines

On many computers, built-in matrix routines are available in BASIC. However, since these routines require considerable storage, they are not always available on microcomputers. Nevertheless they are a useful tool, especially in the context of matrix methods and linear algebraic equations (see Reference 4) and indeed use will be made of them in Chapter 6 (since numerical methods for boundary-value problems lead to systems of linear algebraic equations).

Great care needs to be taken in the correct dimensioning of subscripted variables referred to in matrix routines, via DIM statements. Every element $A(I,J)$ of a matrix A with M rows and N columns has two subscripts, the row and column numbers. It is also recommended that the manual appropriate to a particular computer should be studied, since details vary between computers. For example, some computers require a vector X with 10 components to be dimensioned as $X(10,1)$ with two subscripts (i.e. 10 rows and 1 column) whenever it is to be pre-multiplied by a square matrix, say $A(10,10)$, while other computers permit just one subscript $X(10)$ to be used.

The main instructions are summarized in Table 1.1. Note that in matrix routines all subscripts are taken to be numbered from 1 upwards (to correspond to row or column numbers). Thus the pair of statements

10 DIM A(10,10)
20 MAT INPUT A

will input 100 numbers $A(1,1), \ldots, A(1,10), A(2,1), \ldots, A(10,10)$.

Table 1.1. Matrix statements

Mathematics	BASIC	
$A = B$	MAT A = B	
$A = B + C$	MAT A = B + C	
$A = B - C$	MAT A = B - C	
$A = KB$ (K scalar)	MAT A = (K)*B	
$A = BC$	MAT A = B*C	
$A = 0$ (all zeros)	MAT A = ZER	
Read A	MAT READ A	Elements are listed
Input A	MAT INPUT A	individually by rows
Print A	MAT PRINT A	
$A = m$ by n matrix of ones	MAT A = CON(M,N)	
$A = B^T$	MAT A = TRN(B)	
$A = B^{-1}$	MAT A = INV(B)	
$A = I$	MAT A = IDN	

1.5 Checking and editing programs

If a program has grammatical (syntax) errors in it, then the computer will normally give a clear indication of them. Care needs to be taken, however, to distinguish correctly between the letter 'oh' and the number 'zero' and between 'i' and 'one'. Also mystifying errors may occur if a variable is used for several purposes in the same program.

It is not of course sufficient for a program to be grammatically correct. It must give correct results. It should therefore be tested by using simple test data that give a known solution or by performing hand calculations with simple test data. It is also desirable to ensure that the program cannot go out of control for foolish choices of data, such as a negative number for the number of equations in a problem, and that it is able to cover as wide a range of potential data as possible. It is quite difficult to make programs completely 'userproof', and they become long in doing so. The programs in this book have been kept as short as possible, while providing adequate explanation, and so they are not always userproof.

1.6 Different computers, and variants of BASIC

The algorithms and examples in the book are programmed in a simple version of BASIC that should work on most computers, even those with small storage capacity. Only single-line statements have been used, although many computers allow a number of statements on each line with a separator such as \. Multiple assignments are also sometimes allowed so that, for example, the variables A, B, C, D are each set to zero by the statement

70 A = B = C = D = 0

There is one important area in which computers vary, and this is particularly relevant to microcomputers with visual display units (VDUs). This concerns the number of available columns across each line and the number of rows that are visible on the screen. Simple modifications may be necessary to fit the output of some of the programs in this book on a particular microcomputer. For this purpose 'TAB' printing is a useful facility.

Various enhancements of BASIC have appeared over the years and these are implemented on many computer systems. Indeed the programs in this book could be rewritten to incorporate some of these advanced features. For example, the availability of long variable names (e.g. ROOT instead of say X) can make it easier to write unambiguous programs, although it may be argued that one-character symbols provide a closer link with algebra. Other advanced facilities include more powerful looping with conditional statements, and independent subroutines.

Independent subroutines are particularly valuable in numerical mathematics where one often wishes to call upon a useful program, such as one which solves a set of linear algebraic equations (see Reference 4) in another program. Indeed in Chapter 6 below we must either use BASIC matrix routines to solve the systems of linear equations that occur, or else incorporate the complete text of one of the programs specially developed for such systems in Reference 4 (because of the lack of suitable subroutine facilities in standard BASIC). If and when independent subroutine facilities become available, the programs of Chapter 6 could be suitably modified and simplified.

The use of independent subroutines leads to the disciplines of 'structured programming', in which programs are divided into a number of smaller independent subprograms which are called upon in turn from a main 'driver' program. This greatly eases the task of debugging, since it is often possible to base a new program on a number of old well-tested subprograms.

1.7 Summary of program contents

In writing a BASIC program, the order in which we go about listing instructions is roughly as follows:

(i) REM statements at start (and throughout program) for explanation
(ii) DIM statements for subscripted variables
(iii) DEF statements for function definitions
(iv) READ/INPUT statements for data
(v) *Main program*, with calculations, etc.
(vi) PRINT statements for results
(vii) STOP statement to end calculation (unnecessary at the end of a program)
(viii) Subroutines with RETURN statements
(ix) END statement (optional)

However, although the above order is the one that we use in the present text, since it is universally acceptable, we personally prefer (on a BASIC system which permits this) to place DEF statements before subroutines at the end of the program. Indeed the latter convention has been adopted in earlier texts of this series such as Reference 4.

1.8 References

1. KEMENY, J.G. and KURTZ, T.E., *BASIC Programming*, John Wiley (1968)
2. MONRO, D.M., *Interactive Computing with BASIC*, Edward Arnold (1974)
3. ALCOCK, D., *Illustrating BASIC*, Cambridge University Press (1977)
4. MASON, J.C., *BASIC Matrix Methods*, Butterworths (1984)

Chapter 2

Introduction to differential equations

ESSENTIAL THEORY

Very early in our training, we realize that *equations* are right at the heart of mathematics and of many other scientific subjects. Indeed, the word 'equation' has of late become fashionable amongst politicians and media men, who wish to add a touch of scientific class to their arguments, in such phrases as the 'East–West equation' (though there is sometimes no equation as such involved!). Later in our mathematical education we progress to the key subject of calculus, which is concerned with rates of change or *derivatives* or *differentials*. Again our political and trade union leaders are not slow to demonstrate their scientific credentials, as they lecture us on the subject of differentials in wages, trade, etc. etc. However, their discussion is not really concerned with calculus, and the differential is usually a difference rather than a gradient.

The next step in our mathematical training is to combine equations with calculus. It is then that we come to the subject of differential equations, namely equations which involve differentials. The importance of differential equations is very great indeed, and indeed it is probably true that the majority of all good mathematical models involve such equations. Moreover, most differential equations cannot be solved numerically and accurately without the aid of a computer, and so the subject area of this book is of unquestionable significance.

2.1 Integration

Probably the simplest example of a differential equation is the relation

$$\frac{dy}{dx} = f(x) \tag{2.1}$$

where $f(x)$ is a given function and $y(x)$ is the required function. Here

dy/dx is explicitly known. However, (2.1) is not uniquely solvable as it stands; the solution is

$$y = \int f(x)\,dx + C \tag{2.2}$$

where $\int f(x)\,dx$ denotes an 'indefinite integral' of $f(x)$ and C is a constant of integration. In order to make the value of C specific, we need more information, and we usually impose an 'initial condition' on y of the form

$$y = y_0 \text{ when } x = x_0 \tag{2.3}$$

where x_0, y_0 are given. For example, the solution of the differential equation

$$\frac{dy}{dx} = \sin x \tag{2.4}$$

subject to the initial condition

$$y = 0 \text{ at } x = 0$$

is given by

$$y = 1 - \cos x$$

This solution is deduced by noting that

$$y = \int \sin x\,dx + C = -\cos x + C \tag{2.5}$$

and

$$0 = -1 + C \quad (\text{at } x = 0)$$

We do not intend to pursue the subject of integration any further here, and so we close by making three observations. First, we cannot normally determine an indefinite integral 'analytically' (i.e. in the form of an explicit and exact mathematical function), and almost all integrals have to be determined *approximately* by *numerical methods*. Secondly, a reasonably full introduction to the latter subject is given in Chapter 5 of *BASIC Numerical Mathematics*[1] (abbreviated henceforth to BNM). Thirdly, there is a close analogy between some of the numerical methods used in the present text for solving initial-value problems and the methods of indefinite integration described in the earlier text. For example, the trapezoidal indefinite integration method of Section 5.8 of BNM is a special example of the trapezium rule corrector in Chapter 5 of the present book.

2.2 First order differential equations

A 'first order' differential equation is an equation for $y(x)$ in which the first differential dy/dx (or y') of y occurs, but no higher differentials occur. The general form of such an equation is usually written, by obvious extension of (2.1), as

$$\frac{dy}{dx} = f(x,y) \tag{2.6}$$

where $f(x,y)$ is some given function of the two variables x and y. In words, (2.6) means that at every point P, with coordinates (x,y) in the (x,y) plane, the gradient of y with respect to x is known. This gradient is given by $f(x,y)$, where f is some specified function. In addition, an initial condition is imposed of the form

$$y = y_0 \text{ when } x = x_0 \quad (x_0 \text{ and } y_0 \text{ given}) \tag{2.7}$$

This means that one point P_0 with coordinates (x_0, y_0) is known on the curve.

The above situation is illustrated in *Figure 2.1*. $y(x)$ moves along a curve, and at each point P of this curve the gradient is known. The reader will not (we hope) be surprised to learn that, provided one point P_0 of this curve is given, the remainder of the curve may be determined from the differential equation (2.6), provided that $f(x,y)$ is an appropriately smooth function. (Mathematically, this statement takes the precise form of an 'existence theorem' due to Picard, in which $f(x,y)$ is required to satisfy a 'Lipschitz condition'. See Theorem 3 in Chapter 2 of Reference 2.)

A useful general practical example of (2.6) arises in dynamics, in which x and y represent time and distance, respectively, and y'

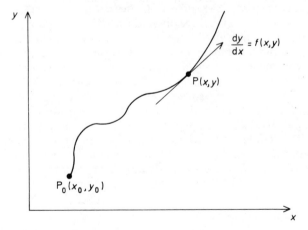

Figure 2.1. $y' = f(x, y)$

measures velocity. Our discussion above implies that, if the velocity of a body is known at every time x and position y (in the form (2.6)), and if some (initial) position y_0 is known at time x_0 (as in (2.7)), then the motion of the body is known for all time.

Let us conclude with an example of a specific problem. Suppose y is given by the differential equation

$$y' = 1 - 2xy \tag{2.8}$$

subject to the initial condition

$$y = 0 \text{ when } x = 0 \quad (\text{i.e. } y(0) = 0) \tag{2.9}$$

Then, as a consequence of our discussion above, the solution y is uniquely determined. In fact it may be expressed as

$$y = e^{-x^2} \int_0^x e^{t^2} \, dt \tag{2.10}$$

(The validity of (2.8) and (2.9) for the function (2.10) may readily be checked.) However, this formula for y is not as explicit as it seems, since it involves an indefinite integral which cannot be determined analytically. Indeed, we have only replaced our problem (2.8), (2.9) by a new problem (2.10), and in practice it is actually preferable to determine y by applying a suitable numerical method to the original problem (2.8)!

2.3 Second order differential equations

A differential equation of the 'second order' is one in which the second differential d^2y/dx^2 (or y'') occurs, but no differentials of higher order occur. The equation, which will typically also involve y and y', thus has the general form

$$y'' = f(x, y, y') \tag{2.11}$$

where f is some given function of the three variables x, y, and y'. For a unique solution y to be determined, it is also necessary to specify two 'boundary conditions' on y, and these might for example take the form of the 'initial conditions'

$$y = y_0 \text{ at } x = x_0 \quad (\text{i.e. } y(x_0) = y_0) \tag{2.12}$$

and

$$y' = y'_0 \text{ at } x = x_0 \quad (\text{i.e. } y'(x_0) = y'_0) \tag{2.13}$$

where x_0, y_0, y'_0 are given constants.

Suppose that (2.11) is taken to be a dynamics equation, with x, y, y', y'' representing time, distance, velocity, and acceleration. Then (2.11) specifies the acceleration at *any* time x as a known function of the time, distance and velocity, and (2.12), (2.13) prescribe the (initial) distance and velocity at time x_0. These suffice to determine the complete motion. For example, if (2.11), (2.12), (2.13) are specifically given as

$$y'' = x - y + 2y' \tag{2.14}$$

$$y(0) = 3 \tag{2.15}$$

$$y'(0) = 3 \tag{2.16}$$

then the unique solution is given by

$$y = (1 + x)e^x + x + 2 \tag{2.17}$$

Again the reader may verify by substitution that y, given by (2.17), satisfies (2.14), (2.15) and (2.16).

Dynamics equations of the second order (2.11) actually tend to occur rather more frequently in practice than those of the first order (2.6). That is because Newton's Second Law, which is almost invariably applied, defines the *acceleration* in terms of the applied force.

2.4 Reduction of second order equations to first order systems

A rather useful trick may be used to reduce *any* differential equation of order more than one to a set of first order equations, but this is achieved at the expense of introducing more dependent variables. In particular the equation (2.11) may be conveniently rewritten, by introducing the new variable

$$z(x) \equiv y', \tag{2.18}$$

as the pair of simultaneous first order equations

$$\left. \begin{array}{l} y' = z \\ z' = f(x,y,z) \end{array} \right\} \tag{2.19}$$

Here y and z ($= y'$) are dependent variables, and x is the independent variable. Moreover, the pair of initial conditions, which involve a derivative, may now be written as a pair of initial conditions without derivatives for y and z:

$$y(x_0) = y_0, \quad z(x_0) = y_0' \tag{2.20}$$

For example, using (2.18) the specific problem (2.14)–(2.16) reduces to the pair of first order equations

$$\left. \begin{array}{l} y' = z \\ z' = x - y + 2z \end{array} \right\} \tag{2.21}$$

subject to the initial conditions

$$y(0)=3, \quad z(0)=3 \tag{2.22}$$

The advantage of this trick is that, in the case of initial-value problems (see below) we can essentially restrict our discussion to the case of *first order* differential equations.

2.5 Systems of first order equations—vector form

The pair of simultaneous equations (2.19) can, by use of vectors, be nicely expressed as a single first order vector differential equation subject to a single vector initial condition. If we write

$$\mathbf{y}=\begin{pmatrix} y \\ z \end{pmatrix}=\begin{pmatrix} y \\ y' \end{pmatrix}$$

$$\mathbf{y}'=\begin{pmatrix} y' \\ z' \end{pmatrix}=\begin{pmatrix} y' \\ y'' \end{pmatrix}$$

then the problem (2.19), (2.20) reduces to the differential equation

$$\mathbf{y}'=\mathbf{f}(x,\mathbf{y}) \tag{2.23}$$

subject to the initial condition

$$\mathbf{y}(x_0)=\begin{pmatrix} y_0 \\ y_0' \end{pmatrix} \tag{2.24}$$

where the 'vector function' $\mathbf{f}$ is defined by

$$\mathbf{f}(x,\mathbf{y})=\mathbf{f}(x,y,z)=\begin{pmatrix} f_1(x,y,z) \\ f_2(x,y,z) \end{pmatrix} \tag{2.25}$$

with

$$f_1(x,y,z)\equiv z, \quad f_2(x,y,z)\equiv f(x,y,z)$$

For example, the specific problem (2.21), (2.22) reduces to

$$\mathbf{y}'=\mathbf{f}(x,\mathbf{y})$$

subject to

$$\mathbf{y}(0)=\begin{pmatrix} 3 \\ 3 \end{pmatrix}$$

where

$$\mathbf{f}(x,\mathbf{y})=\mathbf{f}(x,y,z)=\begin{pmatrix} z \\ x-y+2z \end{pmatrix}$$

2.6 Initial- and boundary-value problems

There are two quite distinct types of problem that may occur, when differential equations of second (or higher) order are involved. If the two additional conditions on y, which are required to solve the problem uniquely, are both specified at the same point x_0 (as was the case in (2.12), (2.13)) then the problem is an 'initial-value problem'. Thus (2.14), (2.15), (2.16) is an initial-value problem.

However, if the two additional conditions are applied at different points, say x_A and x_B, then these conditions are termed 'boundary conditions' and the problem is termed a 'boundary-value problem'. An example of a boundary-value problem is the differential equation

$$y'' = \tfrac{1}{4}\pi^2(x - y) \tag{2.26}$$

subject to the boundary conditions

$$y(0) = 1, \quad y(1) = 1 \tag{2.27}$$

Note that these extra conditions (2.27) are applied at the distinct points $x = 0$ and $x = 1$. In this case, the unique solution is

$$y = x + \cos(\tfrac{1}{2}\pi x) \tag{2.28}$$

2.7 Equations of higher order

In general, a differential equation in $y(x)$ of order p (say) is one in which differentials of order up to and including p occur. With such an equation we must be given a set of p distinct initial conditions or boundary conditions. In the case of an initial-value problem, the same type of trick as was adopted in Section 2.5 may be used to reduce the problem to a set of p simultaneous first order equations. The discussion of the present text (for second order equations) may readily be extended to such problems in a fairly obvious way.

A discussion of boundary-value problems for differential equations of order higher than two is beyond the scope of this book.

2.8 References

1. MASON, J.C., *BASIC Numerical Mathematics*, Butterworths (1983)
2. BURKILL, J.C., *The Theory of Ordinary Differential Equations*, Oliver and Boyd, London (1962)

PROBLEMS

(2.1) State which of the following differential equations may be solved analytically (i.e. by a mathematical formula) rather than numerically, and give the relevant solutions.

(i) $y' = x e^{x^2}$, $y(0) = 1$.
(ii) $y' = \log(x^2)$, $y(0) = 1$. [Use indefinite integration.]
(iii) $y' = \cos(x^2)$, $y(0) = 1$.

(2.2)
(i) By integrating $(1+y^2)^{-1}\, dy = dx$, determine the solution of the initial-value problem

$$y' = 1 + y^2, \quad y(0) = 0.$$

(ii) By noting that

$$\frac{d}{dx}(y^2 e^x) = \left(2y\frac{dy}{dx} + y^2\right)e^x$$

and

$$\frac{d}{dx}[(x-1)e^x] = xe^x$$

determine the solution of the initial-value problem

$$2y\frac{dy}{dx} = x - y^2, \quad y(0) = 1$$

(2.3)
(i) Verify that (2.17) is the solution of the differential equation (2.14) subject to the initial conditions (2.15), (2.16).
(ii) Verify that (2.28) is the unique solution of (2.26), (2.27).

(2.4)
(i) Express the second order (Thomas–Fermi) equation $y'' = x^{-\frac{1}{2}}y^{\frac{3}{2}}$, subject to $y(0) = 1$, $y'(0) = -1.5880710$, as a first order system and give its vector form.
(ii) Express the third order (Blasius) equation $y''' = y''y$, subject to the initial conditions $y(0) = 1$, $y'(0) = 0$, $y''(0) = 1$, as a system of three simultaneous first order equations and give its vector form. [Hint: Define new dependent variables $z = y'$ and $w = y''$.)

Chapter 3

Numerical mathematics and finite differences

ESSENTIAL THEORY

We have already observed that only a very limited range of differential equations can be integrated analytically. It is therefore essential in practice that numerical techniques should be mastered, and that algorithms based on these techniques should be developed and studied.

A thorough treatment of the ideas which underlie numerical mathematics has already been given in *BASIC Numerical Mathematics*[1]. However, it is appropriate that an independent but short discussion should be given here, with an emphasis on aspects and applications relevant to differential equations.

A key topic, which is needed in the discussion of numerical methods for differential equations, is that of *finite differences*, and so their properties will be summmarized at the end of the chapter. A fuller discussion of finite differences may be found in Reference 1.

3.1 The task

Numerical mathematics is concerned with obtaining the actual numerical values of the solution to a given mathematical problem.

This task may conveniently be divided into two main aspects:

(i) to *find a feasible numerical method* for determining the solution approximately
(ii) to *analyse* both the method and the computed solution.

We refer to the aspects (i) and (ii) under the broad titles of 'numerical methods' and 'numerical analysis'. Both of these aspects are vital and should always be taken into account.

It is not at present clear, however, what constitutes a 'feasible' method, and so this is the first question that we must address.

3.1.1 Numerical methods

The key requirements of a feasible numerical method are:

  (i) that it should be *efficient*
 (ii) that it should involve a *finite* number of steps
(iii) that it should be reasonably *simple and convenient*.

At present there is a tendency to judge methods almost entirely by their efficiency. However, we must increasingly take into account our own convenience and time and also the simplicity (and hence storage requirements) of the computer program that corresponds to the method, and that is why we have included requirement (iii). Indeed we might even envisage situations in which requirement (iii) could be more important than requirement (i).

Standard mathematical techniques do not always give feasible numerical methods. For example, for the solution of the first order differential equation

$$y' = f(x,y), \quad y(x_0) = y_0 \text{ (given)} \tag{3.1}$$

a simple mathematical idea might be to use the infinite Taylor series expansion

$$y(x_1) = y(x_0) + hy'(x_0) + \frac{h^2}{2!}y''(x_0) + \ldots + \frac{h^n}{n!}y^{(n)}(x_0) + \ldots \tag{3.2}$$

(where $h = x_1 - x_0$) to calculate $y(x_1)$ for x_1 close to x_0. The point x_1 could then become the new reference point (in place of x_0), and a Taylor series could be used to move to a new point x_2, and so on. The derivatives y'', y''', ... in (3.2) would be calculated (at $x = x_0$) by differentiating (3.1) sufficiently often with respect to x. For example, denoting $\partial f/\partial x$ by f_x, $\partial^2 f/\partial x \partial y$ by f_{xy}, etc., differentiation gives

$$y'' = f_x + y'f_y = f_x + ff_y \tag{3.3}$$

$$y''' = (f_{xx} + f_x f_y + ff_{yx}) + (f_{xy} + f_y^2 + ff_{yy})y'$$
$$= (f_{xx} + 2ff_{xy} + f^2 f_{yy}) + (f_x f_y + ff_y^2) \tag{3.4}$$

etc.

To conform with requirement (i), only a limited number of terms, say up to and including the term in h^n, would be used in (3.2). However, it is clear from (3.3), (3.4) that the algebra involved in determining y'', y''', etc. is rather complicated for a general $f(x,y)$. Indeed a symbolic mathematical technique would in general be needed in order to calculate $y^{(n)}$ for any n, and such techniques involve considerable computation. It is therefore inefficient in general to use a

Taylor series method, and we would not at present classify this method as feasible for the general problem (3.1).

3.1.2 Numerical analysis

The main requirement in numerical analysis is to study the *error* between the computed solution and the true solution. In particular it is necessary to carry out an error analysis, in order to place a quantitative bound on all errors and to estimate such errors. If an error analysis is performed before the calculation of the numerical solution (and hence without reference to it), then it is termed an *'a priori'* error analysis. However, if the error analysis is performed after the numerical solution (and based on that solution), then it is termed an *'a posteriori'* error analysis. It is important to quantify the types of error that occur in a numerical method, and so this topic will be discussed next.

3.2 Sources of error

The three main sources of error, apart from human error, are (i) *data error*, (ii) *truncation error* and (iii) *rounding error*. These relate, respectively, to three key aspects of numerical analysis: (i) *conditioning*, (ii) *convergence*, and (iii) *stability*.

Data errors, or errors in the statement of the problem, must generally be assumed to be present. For example, $f(x,y)$ in (3.1) might (for varying x,y) be regarded as data and only be known approximately. Similarly the initial value $y(x_0)$ might also be in error. Such errors may or may not have a significant effect on the solution of the problem. If a small error in the data leads to a large error in the solution, then we classify the problem as 'ill conditioned'; if it leads only to a small error in the solution, then we classify the problem as 'well conditioned'. For example, the problem

$$y'' - 9y' - 10y = 0 \tag{3.5}$$

with boundary conditions

$$y(0) = 1, \quad y'(0) = -1 \tag{3.6}$$

has the exact solution

$$y = y^{(1)} = e^{-x} \tag{3.7}$$

However, if the initial conditions (3.6) are changed to

$$y(0) = 1, \quad y'(0) = -0.989 \tag{3.8}$$

then the exact solution becomes

$$y = y^{(2)} = 0.999e^{-x} + 0.001\,e^{10x} \tag{3.9}$$

The functions (3.7) and (3.9) differ considerably as x increases.
For example, at $x = 1$,

$$y^{(1)} = e^{-1} = 0.3679$$

$$y^{(2)} = 0.999e^{-1} + 0.001\,e^{10} = 22.39$$

and so the initial-value problem (3.5), (3.6) would be classified as ill conditioned.

Clearly, then, data errors can have serious consequences for a problem that is ill conditioned, and so we must be frank and honest in recognizing ill conditioning. Moreover, we note that ill conditioning, which is a feature of the problem, cannot be eliminated by changing to a new method, unless perhaps the new method corresponds to a restatement of the problem in a well conditioned form.

Truncation errors, by way of contrast, are a feature of the method rather than of the problem. A truncation error is an error which results from the replacement of an infinite process by a finite process with say n steps. For example, if the Taylor series method is used to solve the initial-value problem

$$(1 + x)y' = 1, \quad y(0) = 0 \tag{3.10}$$

then the approximation solution y_n at the point x (close to 0) is expressed as

$$y_n = x - x^2/2 + x^3/3 - \ldots + (-1)^{n-1}x^n/n \tag{3.11}$$

by truncating the infinite series for the true solution

$$y = x - x^2/2 + x^3/3 - \ldots \tag{3.12}$$

In this case the truncation error is known 'exactly' to be

$$y - y_n = (-1)^n x^{n+1}/(n+1) + (-1)^{n+1}x^{n+2}/(n+2) + \ldots$$

Clearly in this case $y - y_n$ approaches zero as n approaches infinity, provided x is in the range $-1 < x < 1$, as a consequence of the convergence of the series (3.12), and so we say that the numerical method (3.11) is convergent. More generally, a numerical method is *convergent* if the truncation error approaches zero as the number n of steps approaches infinity. Convergence is an essential prerequisite of all numerical methods for solving differential equations.

Finally, rounding error is that error which occurs during the computer implementation of a method, as a consequence of the use of inexact computer arithmetic throughout the calculation. In general, all arithmetic operations are performed inexactly, so as to maintain a fixed number of significant digits at each stage of the calculation and for each variable involved. For example, using six significant decimal digits, we might obtain

$$0.456789 \times 1.00001 = 0.456794$$

where the true result is 0.45679356789, and hence incur a rounding error of about 0.0000005 or five in the seventh figure. (In practice, *binary* arithmetic is used, but the effect is similar.)

Significance error is a serious form of rounding error, resulting from the subtraction of two nearly equal numbers. For example, using six significant decimal arithmetic, the calculation

$$6.54321 - 6.54320 = 0.00001$$

leads to a solution correct to perhaps *one* significant figure. Here the true calculation might be

$$6.543214 - 6.543196 = 0.000018$$

and in that case the percentage error committed would be about 44 per cent.

At any stage of a calculation, the sum total of all rounding errors so far committed is termed the *accumulated rounding error*. This accumulated error may or may not grow relative to the solution (at that stage of the calculation). If it does then the method is said to be *unstable*, and if it does not then the method is said to be *stable*. Stability is an important requirement of any method for the solution of differential equations; in particular, many numerical methods introduce spurious solutions in addition to correct solutions, and instability occurs when the spurious solutions swamp the correct solutions.

It is not easy to illustrate instability at such an early stage of this book, and indeed the subject will be dealt with more specifically in later chapters when numerical methods are described in detail. However, we might refer again to the problem (3.5), (3.6), and note that numerical methods may be invented which do not exactly satisfy the derivative boundary condition $y'(0) = -1$. Such methods are likely to be unstable for this problem, since we have already shown above that a small change in $y'(0)$ yields a large change in y (as x increases).

3.3 Well-posed problems

Finally, we must observe that it is essential, before embarking on the numerical solution of a problem, to ascertain that it is a well-posed problem, namely a problem which has a unique and meaningful solution. It is not at all difficult to fall into the trap of attempting to solve ill-posed problems for differential equations. For example, consider the initial-value problem

$$yy'' = y' \tag{3.13}$$

subject to the boundary conditions

$$y(0) = 0, \quad y'(0) = 1 \tag{3.14}$$

On the surface this might appear to be a 'normal' second order differential equation with two typical initial conditions. However, the particular equation (3.13) tells us already that, whenever y is zero, so also is y', and so the initial conditions (3.14) are in fact impossible to satisfy. Indeed, if we insist on the initial condition $y(0) = 0$, then it is far from easy to decide just what other initial conditions may be imposed! On the other hand, we may uniquely solve (3.13) near $x = 0$ for the initial conditions

$$y(0) = 1, \quad y'(0) = 1$$

3.4 Summary

Figure 3.1, which has already appeared in the text *BASIC Matrix Methods*, provides a useful check-list of the various steps that characterize the implementation of an ideal numerical method.

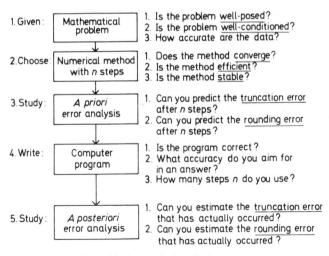

Figure 3.1 Steps in an ideal numerical method.

3.5 Finite differences

Define equally spaced ordinates (or stations) x_i at steps of h and corresponding abscissae y_i by

$$x_i = x_0 + ih, \quad y_i = y(x_i) \tag{3.15}$$

and extend this definition to include intermediate ordinates x_p (any real p) by writing

$$x_p = x_0 + ph, \quad y_p = y(x_p) \tag{3.16}$$

For example, $x_{\frac{1}{2}} = x_0 + h/2$ and $y_{\frac{1}{2}} = y(x_{\frac{1}{2}})$.

Then the *forward difference* Δy_i, *backward difference* ∇y_i and *central difference* δy_i of y_i at x_i are defined by

$$\Delta y_i = y_{i+1} - y_i, \quad \nabla y_i = y_i - y_{i-1}, \quad \delta y_i = y_{i+\frac{1}{2}} - y_{i-\frac{1}{2}} \tag{3.17}$$

and all these differences are approximations to hy'_i (see Reference 1), where $y'_p, y''_p, \ldots$ denote $y', y'', \ldots$ evaluated at $x = x_p$.

If the *mean value operator* μ is now defined by

$$\mu y_i = \tfrac{1}{2}(y_{i-\frac{1}{2}} + y_{i+\frac{1}{2}}) \tag{3.18}$$

then it follows that the *mean central difference* operator $\mu\delta$ is given by

$$\mu\delta y_i = \tfrac{1}{2}(y_{i+1} - y_{i-1}) \tag{3.19}$$

Second differences may next be expressed in the form

$$\begin{aligned}
\Delta^2 y_i &= \Delta(\Delta y_i) = y_{i+2} - 2y_{i+1} + y_i \\
\nabla^2 y_i &= \nabla(\nabla y_i) = y_i - 2y_{i-1} + y_{i-2} \\
\delta^2 y_i &= \delta(\delta y_i) = y_{i+1} - 2y_i + y_{i-1}
\end{aligned} \tag{3.20}$$

and third and higher differences may similarly be evaluated.

In the context of numerical methods for differential equations of first and second order, a key step is to approximate y' and y'' by using finite differences. The errors in such formulae are typically determined by using Taylor series.

For example

$$y_{i+1} = y(x_{i+1}) = y(x_i + h) \quad = y(x_i) + hy'(x_i) + \frac{h^2}{2!}y''(x_i) + \ldots$$

i.e.

$$y_{i+1} = y_i + hy'_i + \frac{h^2}{2!}y''_i + \frac{h^3}{3!}y'''_i + \ldots \tag{3.21}$$

Thus

$$y_{i+1} - y_i = hy'_i + O(h^2)$$

and so

$$y'_i = h^{-1}\Delta y_i + O(h) \tag{3.22}$$

Similarly

$$y_{i-1} = y(x_i - h) = y_i - hy'_i + \frac{h^2}{2!}y''_i - \frac{h^3}{3!}y'''_i + \ldots \tag{3.23}$$

From (3.21) and (3.23) we deduce that

$$y_{i+1} - y_{i-1} = 2hy'_i + O(h^3)$$

and hence

$$y'_i = (2h)^{-1}\mu\delta y_i + O(h^2) \tag{3.24}$$

Also, from (3.20), (3.21) and (3.23),

$$y_{i+1} - 2y_i + y_{i-1} = \delta^2 y_i = h^2 y''_i + O(h^4)$$

Thus

$$y''_i = (h^2)^{-1}\delta^2 y_i + O(h^2) \tag{3.25}$$

Summarizing the results (3.22), (3.24), (3.25), the first derivative y'_i of y at x_i may be approximated with a forward difference with accuracy proportional to h:

$$y'_i = \frac{1}{h}(y_{i+1} - y_i) + O(h) \tag{3.26}$$

Consistent and higher accuracy, however, proportional to h^2 may be obtained to both first and second derivatives y'_i, y''_i of y at x_i by using central differences:

$$y'_i = \frac{1}{2h}(y_{i+1} - y_{i-1}) + O(h^2) \tag{3.27}$$

$$y''_i = \frac{1}{h^2}(y_{i+1} - 2y_i + y_{i+1}) + O(h^2) \tag{3.28}$$

We have used the order notation $O(h^k)$ above, as in Reference 1, and we conclude with some formal revision of this. By $O(h^k)$ we mean a series in powers of h, in which the lowest power of h occurring is h^k. For example, the series

$$\frac{h^4}{4!} + \frac{h^5}{5!} + \frac{h^6}{6!} + \dots \tag{3.29}$$

is $O(h^4)$. Clearly a term of order h^k, i.e. $O(h^k)$, is proportional to h^k. Moreover, for h sufficiently small,

$$O(h^k) \simeq Ah^k$$

where A is some constant. For example, for h small, (3.29) is proportional to h^4 and approximately equal to $h^4/4!$.

3.6 Reference

1. MASON, J.C., *BASIC Numerical Mathematics*, Butterworths (1983).

Chapter 4

Elementary linear problems

ESSENTIAL THEORY

4.1 Introduction—linear and non-linear equations

Differential equations come in a multitude of forms, and so it is important to recognize the various types and make appropriate classifications. In Chapter 2 we classified equations according to their *order* (first order, second order, etc.), and it is equally important to classify them either as linear or as non-linear equations. A linear equation is one in which y and its derivatives $y', y'', \ldots$ appear only 'as themselves', i.e. not raised to a power and not within another function. Thus a *linear* equation of order n has the general form

$$a_0(x)y^{(n)} + a_1(x)y^{(n-1)} + \ldots + a_{n-1}(x)y' + a_n(x)y = f(x) \qquad (4.1)$$

where $a_0, a_1, \ldots, a_n, f$ are given functions of x. A specific example is the equation

$$y' + y = x$$

Throughout this book, dashes denote derivatives with respect to x ($y' = \mathrm{d}y/\mathrm{d}x$, $y'' = \mathrm{d}^2y/\mathrm{d}x^2$, $\ldots$, $y^{[n]} = \mathrm{d}^ny/\mathrm{d}x^n$).

The function $f(x)$ on the right-hand side is commonly known as a *forcing function*. A *non-linear* equation, on the other hand, is any equation which is not linear and one example is the Thomas–Fermi equation

$$y'' = x^{-\frac{1}{2}} y^{\frac{3}{2}}$$

In the present chapter we restrict our attention to *linear* differential equations of the first and second orders and use methods of solution which are essentially *analytical* rather than numerical in nature.

We may further classify linear equations into homogeneous or non-homogenous ones. Specially (4.1) is *homogeneous* if the forcing function ($f(x)$) is identically zero, and *non-homogeneous* otherwise. For example, the equations

$$y' - y = x, \quad y'' - 2y' + y = 0 \qquad (4.2)$$

31

are respectively non-homogeneous and homogeneous. We may also consider further simplifications of the left-hand side in (4.1), and in particular an *equation with constant coefficients* is one in which $a_0, a_1,$ ..., a_n do not vary with x. Both of the equations in (4.2) are of this type.

It is also common to make qualitative categorizations of differential equations into those which are respectively easy, difficult or impossible to solve (by analytical rather than numerical methods). Almost all non-linear problems fall into the impossible category.

In fact we restrict attention here to equations with constant coefficients, for equations with variable coefficients typically require the use of infinite series and the numerical evaluations of such series can often cause computational errors at least as great as those arising from a purely numerical solution. Computer programs which implement series methods are therefore increasingly based on exact *symbolic mathematical programming* systems (such as MACSYMA, REDUCE, MAPLE, etc.), and a discussion of this topic is beyond the scope of this book. Even with a restriction to constant-coefficient equations, it becomes apparent that only a limited range of non-homogeneous problems can be solved easily, and so an early recourse to numerical techniques is required in this book.

4.2 First order equations—integrating factors

We can normally assume that a linear first order equation may be written in the general form

$$\frac{dy}{dx} + P(x)y = Q(x) \tag{4.3}$$

(by dividing both sides of (4.1) (for $n=1$) by $a_0(x)$), where P and Q are given functions. It is then possible, in principle, to simplify the problem by multiplying both sides of (4.3) by the *integrating factor*

$$R(x) \equiv \exp[\int P(x)\,dx] \tag{4.4}$$

and then integrating with respect to x. This gives

$$yR(x) = \int Q(x)R(x)\,dx + A \tag{4.5}$$

where A is a constant of integration. Hence the *general solution* of (4.3) is

$$y = [R(x)]^{-1}\int QR\,dx + A[R(x)]^{-1} \tag{4.6}$$

where R is defined by (4.4). We have thus obtained an explicit form for y, involving one arbitrary constant A. A specific value of A for

(4.6) could be determined uniquely by specifying an *initial condition* for y, such as

$$y(x_0) = y_0 \quad (x_0, y_0 \text{ given})$$

For example, consider the first order equation

$$xy' + y = \ln x \tag{4.7}$$

subject to the condition

$$y(1) = 0 \tag{4.8}$$

Then, dividing by x, (4.7) may be written in the form (4.3) as

$$y' + (1/x)y = (1/x)\ln x \tag{4.9}$$

with $P(x) = 1/x$ and $Q(x) = (1/x)\ln x$.

The integrating factor $R(x)$, by (4.4), is

$$R(x) = \exp \int (1/x)\,dx = \exp(\ln x) = x$$

Also

$$\int Q(x)\,R(x)\,dx = \int \ln x\,d x$$
$$= x \ln x - \int x(1/x)\,dx = x(\ln x - 1)$$

on integrating by parts, and hence from (4.6) the *general solution* of (4.7) is

$$y = x^{-1}x(\ln x - 1) + Ax^{-1} = \ln x - 1 + A/x \tag{4.10}$$

where A is an arbitrary constant.

The validity of (4.10) is readily verified by substitution into (4.7). The required value of A is obtained by applying (4.8) to (4.10):

$$0 = \ln 1 - 1 + A/1 \Rightarrow A = 1$$

Hence the unique solution of (4.7) subject to the initial condition (4.8) is

$$y = \ln x - 1 + 1/x \tag{4.11}$$

However, the above method is not as universally useful as it looks, since the two required indefinite integrals, namely those of $P(x)$ and of $Q(x)R(x)$, can only be determined analytically in a rather limited selection of cases. Indeed, in general, numerical methods would be needed for these integrals, and in that case the methods of Chapter 5 below are likely to be more appropriate.

4.2.1 Constant-coefficient equations

In order to make progress in an analytical context, let us assume that

$P(x)$ is constant, so that (4.3) is a *constant-coefficient linear equation*. We shall also assume that $Q(x)$ is equal to an exponential, sine, or cosine function. This is still a problem of some practical relevance, and indeed important electrical circuit problems have precisely this form. The differential equation now has the form

$$y' + \lambda y = f(x) \tag{4.12}$$

with $f(x)$ defined as one of the following functions (r,s given):

$$\left.\begin{array}{l} \text{(i) } f(x) = 0 \\ \text{(ii) } f(x) = e^{rx} \\ \text{(iii) } f(x) = a \cos sx + b \sin sx \end{array}\right\} \tag{4.13}$$

We specify as an initial condition, so as to determine a unique solution,

$$y(x_0) = y_0 \quad (x_0, y_0 \text{ given}) \tag{4.14}$$

From (4.12) we see that $P(x) = \lambda$ and hence, from (4.4), the *integrating factor* is

$$R(x) \equiv e^{\lambda x} \tag{4.15}$$

We leave the reader with the exercise of obtaining from (4.5) the following general solutions corresponding to the three choices (4.13) of $f(x)$:

$$\left.\begin{array}{l} \text{(i) } y = A e^{-\lambda x} \\ \text{(ii) (a) } y = (r + \lambda)^{-1} e^{rx} + A e^{-\lambda x} \quad \text{if } r \neq -\lambda \\ \\ \quad\quad \text{(b) } y = (A + x) e^{-\lambda x} \quad\quad\quad\quad \text{if } r = -\lambda \\ \text{(iii) } y = A e^{-\lambda x} + (\lambda^2 + s^2)^{-1}[(a\lambda - bs)\cos sx \\ \quad\quad\quad + (as + b\lambda)\sin sx] \end{array}\right\} \tag{4.16}$$

The parameter A in (4.16) is an arbitrary constant which may be determined uniquely from the initial condition (4.14). The reader will readily verify that the respective values of A are

$$\left.\begin{array}{l} \text{(i) } A = e^{\lambda x_0} y_0 \\ \text{(ii) (a) } A = e^{\lambda x_0} y_0 - (r + \lambda)^{-1} e^{\lambda x_0} \quad \text{if } r \neq -\lambda \\ \\ \quad\quad \text{(b) } A = e^{\lambda x_0} y_0 - x_0 \quad\quad\quad\quad\quad \text{if } r = -\lambda \\ \text{(iii) } A = e^{\lambda x_0} y_0 - (\lambda^2 + s^2)^{-1} e^{\lambda x_0}[(a\lambda - bs)\cos sx_0 \\ \quad\quad\quad + (as + b\lambda)\sin sx_0] \end{array}\right\} \tag{4.17}$$

As an example, consider

$$y' + 4y = \sin x, \quad y(\pi) = 1 \tag{4.18}$$

namely (4.12)–(4.14) with the choice $\lambda = 4$ and

(iii) $f(x) = \sin x \ (a = 0, \ b = s = 1)$ and $x_0, y_0 = \pi, 1$

From (4.16), (4.17) we deduce that

$$y = A e^{-4x} + (17)^{-1}(4 \sin x - \cos x)$$

where

$$A = e^{4\pi} - (17^{-1})e^{4\pi}(4 \sin \pi - \cos \pi) = 16 e^{4\pi}/17$$

Hence

$$y = \tfrac{1}{17}[16 e^{4(\pi - x)} + 4 \sin x - \cos x] \tag{4.19}$$

4.2.2 BASIC program for constant coefficients

For our first program we generate the explicit solutions of (4.12)–(4.14) in the respective forms (4.16) and (4.17).

Algorithm 4.1   Solution of $y' + \lambda y = f(x)$

Input λ for (4.12) and specify the form (4.13) (i), (ii) or (iii) for $f(x)$.
Specify constants r,s as well as a,b (if required).
Specify the initial values (x_0, y_0) for the initial conditions (4.14).
Output the solution by combining (4.16) and (4.17) for the respect-
ive case (i), (ii) or (iii).

Program 4.1 FIRGEN: General first order constant-coefficient
equations

```
LIST
FIRGEN

10      REM- FIRGEN: SOLVES GENERAL FIRST ORDER CONSTANT
20      REM- COEFFICIENT EQUATION    Y'+LAMBDA*Y=F(X)
30      REM- WITH ANY OF 3 CHOICES FOR F(X) :    (1) F(X)=0
40      REM- (2) F(X)=EXP(RX)  (3) F(X)=A COS(SX)+B SIN(SX)
50      REM-  INITIAL CONDITION:  Y(X0)=Y0.
60      PRINT 'Y'+LY=F(X) ;   INPUT L';
70      INPUT L
80      PRINT 'INPUT INITIAL VALUES X0,Y0';
90      INPUT X0,Y0
100     PRINT 'FORM OF F(X) ALLOWED:'
110     PRINT '(A) F(X)=0'
120     PRINT '(B) F(X)=EXP(RX)'
130     PRINT '(C) F(X)=A COS(SX)+B SIN(SX)'
140     PRINT
150     PRINT 'INPUT A,B,OR C';
160     INPUT ANS$
170     IF ANS$='A' THEN GOSUB 210
180     IF ANS$='B' THEN GOSUB 280
190     IF ANS$='C' THEN GOSUB 440
200     GO TO 560
210     PRINT 'F(X)=0'
220     PRINT 'GENERAL SOLN OF EQN:'
230     PRINT 'Y=A*EXP('i'-L;'X)'
240     A=Y0*EXP(L*X0)
250     PRINT 'UNIQUE SOLN OF INIT CONDNS:'
260     PRINT 'Y='iAi'EXP('i'-L;'X)'
270     RETURN
```

```
280      PRINT "F(X)=EXP(RX)"
290      PRINT "INPUT R";
300      INPUT R
310      PRINT "GENERAL SOLN OF EQN:"
320      IF (R+L) =0 THEN 390
330      C=1/(R+L)
340      PRINT "Y=";C;"EXP(";R;"X)+A*EXP(";-L;"X)"
350      A=EXP(L*XO)*(YO-C*EXP(R*XO))
360      PRINT "UNIQUE SOLN OF INIT CONDNS:"
370      PRINT "Y=";C;"EXP(";R;"X)+";A;"EXP(";-L;"X)"
380      GO TO 430
390      PRINT "Y=(A+X)EXP(";-L;"X)"
400      A=EXP(L*XO)*YO-XO
410      PRINT "UNIQUE SOLN OF INIT CONDNS:"
420      PRINT "Y=(";A;"+X)EXP(";-L;"X)"
430      RETURN
440      PRINT "F(X)=A COS(SX)+B SIN(SX)"
450      PRINT "INPUT A,B,S";
460      INPUT A,B,S
470      PRINT "GENERAL SOLN OF EQN:"
480      C=1/(L*L+S*S)
490      D=(A*L-B*S)*C
500      E=(A*S+B*L)*C
510      PRINT "Y=A*EXP(";-L;"X)+(";D;"COS(";S;"X)+";E;"SIN(";S;"X))"
520      A=EXP(L*XO)*(YO-D*COS(S*XO)-E*SIN(S*XO))
530      PRINT "UNIQUE SOLN OF INIT CONDNS:"
540      PRINT "Y=";A;"EXP(";-L;"X)+(";D;"COS(";S;"X)+";E;"SIN(";S;"X))"
550      RETURN
560      END
```

Sample run 1

```
RUN
FIRGEN

Y'+LY=F(X) ;   INPUT L? 4
INPUT INITIAL VALUES XO,YO? 0,1
FORM OF F(X) ALLOWED:
(A) F(X)=0
(B) F(X)=EXP(RX)
(C) F(X)=A COS(SX)+B SIN(SX)

INPUT A,B,OR C? A
F(X)=0
GENERAL SOLN OF EQN:
Y=A*EXP(-4 X)
UNIQUE SOLN OF INIT CONDNS:
Y= 1 EXP(-4 X)
Ready
```

Sample run 2

```
RUN
FIRGEN

Y'+LY=F(X) ;   INPUT L? -4
INPUT INITIAL VALUES XO,YO? 0,1
FORM OF F(X) ALLOWED:
(A) F(X)=0
(B) F(X)=EXP(RX)
(C) F(X)=A COS(SX)+B SIN(SX)

INPUT A,B,OR C? B
F(X)=EXP(RX)
INPUT R? 5
GENERAL SOLN OF EQN:
Y= 1 EXP( 5 X)+A*EXP( 4 X)
UNIQUE SOLN OF INIT CONDNS:
Y= 1 EXP( 5 X)+ 0 EXP( 4 X)
Ready
```

Sample run 3

```
RUN
FIRGEN

Y'+LY=F(X) ;   INPUT L? -4
INPUT INITIAL VALUES X0,Y0? -1,0
FORM OF F(X) ALLOWED:
(A) F(X)=0
(B) F(X)=EXP(RX)
(C) F(X)=A COS(SX)+B SIN(SX)

INPUT A,B,OR C? B
F(X)=EXP(RX)
INPUT R? 4
GENERAL SOLN OF EQN:
Y=(A+X)EXP( 4 X)
UNIQUE SOLN OF INIT CONDNS:
Y=( 1 +X)EXP( 4 X)
Ready
```

Sample run 4

```
RUN
FIRGEN

Y'+LY=F(X) ;   INPUT L? 1
INPUT INITIAL VALUES X0,Y0? 0,1
FORM OF F(X) ALLOWED:
(A) F(X)=0
(B) F(X)=EXP(RX)
(C) F(X)=A COS(SX)+B SIN(SX)

INPUT A,B,OR C? C
F(X)=A COS(SX)+B SIN(SX)
INPUT A,B,S? 1,1,3
GENERAL SOLN OF EQN:
Y=A*EXP(-1 X)+(-.2 COS( 3 X)+ .4 SIN( 3 X))
UNIQUE SOLN OF INIT CONDNS:
Y= 1.2 EXP(-1 X)+(-.2 COS( 3 X)+ .4 SIN( 3 X))
Ready
```

Program notes

(1) The program chooses one of the forms (i), (ii), (iii) of (4.13) by inputting the character A, B, or C (respectively).

(2) The program executes the subroutines on lines 210–270, 280–430, 440–550 according as the forms (i), (ii) or (iii) are chosen. These subroutines execute the formulae (4.16), (4.17) in the respective cases.

(3) The sample runs illustrate solutions for each of the cases (i), (ii)(a), (ii)(b), (iii) of (4.16), in that order.

The solutions are, respectively,

$$y = A\,e^{-4x} \text{ with } A = 1$$

$$y = e^{5x} + A\,e^{4x} \text{ with } A = 0$$

$$y = (A + x)e^{4x} \text{ with } A = 1$$

$$y = A\,e^{-x} + 0.1(-2\cos 3x + 4\sin 3x) \text{ with } A = 1 - 0.1(-2) = 1.2$$

4.3 Second order equations—constant coefficients

Clearly we must expect second order differential equations, i.e. ones involving y'', to be harder to solve analytically than first order equations, and so we immediately restrict attention to a constant-coefficient equation of the form

$$ay'' + by' + cy = f(x) \tag{4.20}$$

where a,b,c are given real constants and $f(x)$ is a given forcing function. Then (see Reference 1, for example) the *general solution* of (4.20) may be written as the *sum* of two parts, namely:

(i) the *complementary function*, which is the general solution of the corresponding 'homogeneous' equation

$$ay'' + by' + cy = 0 \tag{4.21}$$

(i.e. (4.20) with $f(x) = 0$)

(ii) a *particular integral* (or particular solution) of the original non-homogeneous equation (4.20).

The complementary function (and hence the general solution) involves *two arbitrary constants*.

For example, the general solution of

$$y'' + y = x \tag{4.22}$$

is

$$y = A \cos x + B \sin x + x \tag{4.23}$$

where A,B are arbitrary constants.

This solution is the sum of the complementary function $A \cos x + B \sin x$, which happens to be the general solution of the 'equation of simple harmonic motion' $y'' + y = 0$, and a particular integral $y = x$ (which is readily seen to satisfy (4.22)).

Values of the two arbitrary constants A,B are uniquely determined by specifying two appropriate initial conditions or boundary conditions. For example, if the initial conditions

$$y(0) = 0, \quad y'(0) = 2 \tag{4.24}$$

are applied in conjunction with the problem (4.22), then we deduce from (4.23) that

$$0 = A, \quad 1 = B$$

and hence

$$y = \sin x + x \tag{4.25}$$

Alternatively, if for example the boundary conditions

$$y(\pi/4)=\pi, \quad y(3\pi/4)=0 \qquad (4.26)$$

are applied to (4.22), then (4.23) gives

$$\pi = A(1/\sqrt{2}) + B(1/\sqrt{2}) + \pi/4 \qquad (4.27)$$

$$0 = A(-1/\sqrt{2}) + B(1/\sqrt{2}) + 3\pi/4$$

In this case we obtain a pair of simultaneous equations for A,B from which we deduce that

$$A = 3\pi/(2\sqrt{2}), \quad B = 0$$

and hence

$$y = \frac{3\pi}{2\sqrt{2}}\cos x + x \qquad (4.28)$$

4.3.1 Complementary functions—homogeneous equations

Our first task is to determine complementary functions, by obtaining the general solution of the homogeneous equation (4.21), namely

$$ay'' + by' + cy = 0 \quad \text{(given } a,b,c)$$

To achieve this, we try to find solutions of the form

$$y = A\,e^{mx} \qquad (4.29)$$

and upon substitution of (4.29) into (4.21) we deduce that

$$e^{mx}(am^2 + bm + c) = 0$$

and hence

$$Q(m) = am^2 + bm + c = 0 \qquad (4.30)$$

The quadratic equation (4.30), known as the *auxiliary equation*, has three possible types of solution (depending on the values of a,b,c) which may be categorized as follows:

(i) If $b^2 > 4ac$, then $Q(m)$ has two distinct roots

$$m = m_1, m_2 = (-b \pm \sqrt{b^2 - 4ac})/(2a) \qquad (4.31)(i)$$

(ii) If $b^2 = 4ac$, then $Q(m)$ has a double real root

$$m = m_1 \text{ twice} = -b/(2a) \qquad (4.31)(ii)$$

(iii) If $b^2 < 4ac$, then $Q(m)$ has complex conjugate roots

$$m = u \pm iv \qquad (4.31)(iii)$$

where

$$u = -b/(2a), \quad v = \sqrt{4ac - b^2}/(2a)$$

For example, the second order equation

$$y'' - 3y' + 2y = 0$$

has the auxiliary equation

$$m^2 - 3m + 2 = 0$$

for which (i) above holds and

$$m = m_1, m_2 = 2,1$$

From (4.29), we note that we have found two solutions

$$e^{2x}, \quad e^x$$

and it is not difficult to deduce (because of the linear form of (4.21)) that the general solution is

$$y = A\,e^{2x} + B\,e^x \quad (A,B \text{ arbitrary})$$

It is similarly easy to deduce in general that, for (4.31)(i), the general solution of (4.21) is

$$y = A\,e^{m_1 x} + B\,e^{m_2 x}$$

However, the cases (4.31)(ii), (4.31)(iii) require more careful attention, and we refer readers to Reference 1 for details. It is not difficult to verify the following forms for the respective general solutions of (4.31)(i), (ii), (iii):

$$\left.\begin{array}{ll} \text{(i)} & y = A\,e^{m_1 x} + B\,e^{m_2 x} \\ \text{(ii)} & y = (A + Bx)e^{m_1 x} \\ \text{(iii)} & y = e^{ux}(A \cos vx + B \sin vx) \end{array}\right\} \qquad (4.32)$$

where A, B are arbitrary constants in each case.

For our next program, we shall assume that $f(x) = 0$ in (4.20), so that there is no particular integral to determine and indeed the complementary function is itself the required general solution. Moreover, we shall first simplify the problem to the special equation

$$y'' + \lambda y = 0 \qquad (4.33)$$

since this is an equation of fundamental importance, which includes the classical equation of simple harmonic motion (when λ is positive). It is easy to deduce, from (4.31), the three cases

$$\begin{array}{lll} \text{(i)} & \lambda < 0, & m_1, m_2 = \pm m \text{ where } m = (-\lambda)^{\frac{1}{2}} \\ \text{(ii)} & \lambda = 0, & m_1 = 0 \text{ twice} \end{array} \qquad (4.34)$$

(iii) $\lambda > 0$, $u = 0, v = \lambda^{\frac{1}{2}}$

The *general solutions* for these three respective cases are

(i) $y = A e^{mx} + B e^{-mx}$
(ii) $y = A + Bx$ (4.35)
(iii) $y = A \cos vx + B \sin vx$

To obtain a unique solution, we need to specify a pair of general boundary conditions, and for this program we consider the *initial* conditions

$$y(x_0) = y_0, \quad y'(x_0) = d_0 \quad (x_0, y_0, d_0 \text{ given})$$ (4.36)

For the respective cases (i), (ii), (iii) of (4.35), we obtain from (4.36) the pairs of simultaneous equations

(i) $y_0 = Ae^{mx_0} + Be^{-mx_0}$, $d_0 = m(Ae^{mx_0} - Be^{-mx_0})$
(ii) $y_0 = A + Bx_0$, $d_0 = B$
(iii) $y_0 = A \cos vx_0 + B \sin vx_0$
       $d_0 = v(-A \sin vx_0 + B \cos vx_0)$

from which we may readily deduce the respective solutions:

(i) $A = e^{-mx_0}(my_0 + d_0)/(2m)$, $B = e^{mx_0}(my_0 - d_0)/(2m)$
(ii) $A = y_0 - d_0 x_0$, $B = d_0$ (4.37)
(iii) $A = (vy_0 \cos vx_0 - d_0 \sin vx_0)/v$
       $B = (vy_0 \sin vx_0 + d_0 \cos vx_0)v$

Algorithm 4.2   Solution of $y'' + \lambda y = 0$; $y(x_0) = y_0$, $y'(x_0) = d_0$

Specify λ, s_0, y_0, d_0 and categorize into case (i), (ii), or (iii).
Define a general solution of (4.33) according to (4.34), (4.35).
Define a unique solution of (4.33), (4.36) according to (4.37).

Program 4.2   SECSPE: Special second order initial-value problems

```
LIST
SECSPE

100     REM- SECSPE: SOLVES SPECIAL SECOND ORDER EQUATION
110     REM- OF FORM     Y''+LAMBDA*Y=0,   WITH INITIAL
120     REM- CONDITIONS    Y(XO)=YO,    Y'(XO)=DO.
130     PRINT "EQUATION   Y''+L*Y=0"
140     PRINT "INPUT L";
150     INPUT L
160     PRINT "INITIAL CONDITIONS AT XO"
170     PRINT "INPUT XO,Y(XO),Y''(XO)";
180     INPUT XO,YO,DO
190     PRINT "GENERAL SOLN OF Y''+LY=0 :"
200     IF L<0 THEN 230
210     IF L=0 THEN 310
220     IF L>0 THEN 370
```

```
230     REM-    CASE (1)
240     M=SQRT(-L)
250     PRINT "Y=A*EXP("iMi"X)+B*EXP(-"iMi"X)"
260     PRINT "UNIQUE SOLN OF INITIAL CONDITIONS:"
270     A=.5*EXP(-M*X0)*(M*Y0+D0)/M
280     B=.5*EXP(M*X0)*(M*Y0-D0)/M
290     PRINT "Y="iAi"EXP("iMi"X)+"iBi"*EXP(-"iMi"X)"
300     GO TO 440
310     REM-    CASE(2)
320     PRINT "Y=A+B*X"
330     PRINT "UNIQUE SOLN OF INITIAL CONDITIONS:"
340     A=Y0-D0*X0
350     PRINT "Y="iAi"+"iD0i"X"
360     GO TO 440
370     REM-    CASE(3)
380     V=SQRT(L)
390     PRINT "Y=A*COS("iVi"X)+B*SIN("iVi"X)"
400     PRINT "UNIQUE SOLN OF INITIAL CONDITIONS:"
410     A=Y0*COS(V*X0)-D0*SIN(V*X0)/V
420     B=Y0*SIN(V*X0)+D0*COS(V*X0)/V
430     PRINT "Y="iAi"COS("iVi"X)+"iBi"SIN("iVi"X)"
440     END
```

Ready

Sample run 1

```
RUN
SECSPE

EQUATION  Y''+L*Y=0
INPUT L? -4
INITIAL CONDITIONS AT X0
INPUT X0,Y(X0),Y''(X0)? .5,1,-2
GENERAL SOLN OF Y''+LY=0 :
Y=A*EXP( 2 X)+B*EXP(- 2 X)
UNIQUE SOLN OF INITIAL CONDITIONS:
Y= 0 EXP( 2 X)+ 2.71828 *EXP(- 2 X)
Ready
```

Sample run 2

```
RUN
SECSPE

EQUATION  Y''+L*Y=0
INPUT L? 0
INITIAL CONDITIONS AT X0
INPUT X0,Y(X0),Y''(X0)? 0,1,1
GENERAL SOLN OF Y''+LY=0 :
Y=A+B*X
UNIQUE SOLN OF INITIAL CONDITIONS:
Y= 1 + 1 X
Ready
```

Sample run 3

```
RUN
SECSPE

EQUATION  Y''+L*Y=0
INPUT L? 9
INITIAL CONDITIONS AT X0
INPUT X0,Y(X0),Y''(X0)? 0.7853982,0,-1
GENERAL SOLN OF Y''+LY=0 :
Y=A*COS( 3 X)+B*SIN( 3 X)
UNIQUE SOLN OF INITIAL CONDITIONS:
Y= .235702 COS( 3 X)+ .235702 SIN( 3 X)
Ready
```

Program notes

(1) The program, which uses 'L' for λ, tests the three cases $L<0$, $L=0$, $L>0$ and carries out the instructions 230–300, 310–360, 370–440 in these respective cases.

(2) The three sample runs test the three types of solution ($L<0$, $L=0$, $L>0$). Run 1 gives

$$y = ee^{-2x}$$

so that

$$y(0.5) = ee^{-1} = 1, \quad y'(0.5) = -2ee^{-1} = -2$$

Run 2 gives

$$y = 1 + x$$

so that

$$y(0) = y'(0) = 1$$

Run 3 gives

$$y = (\cos 3x + \sin 3x)/(3\sqrt{2})$$

so that

$$y(\pi/4) = (-1/\sqrt{2} + 1/\sqrt{2})/(3\sqrt{2}) = 0$$
$$y'(\pi/4) = 3(-1/\sqrt{2} - 1/\sqrt{2})/(3\sqrt{2}) = -1$$

For our third program, we move on to the general constant-coefficient homogeneous problem (4.21), namely

$$ay'' - by' + cy = 0 \quad (a, b, c \text{ given})$$

The general solution of this problem will be determined according to the form (4.32) above.

However, for simplicity, boundary conditions will *not* be included, and so the reader is left to make suitable additions to the program (as were made in Program 4.2) in order to determine unique solutions.

The solution of the quadratic equation

$$Q(m) = am^2 + bm + c = 0$$

might be thought of as a trivial matter. However, it was noted in Reference 2 that numerical difficulties can arise in calculating m_1, m_2 accurately from

$$m = m_1, m_2 = (-b \pm \sqrt{b^2 - 4ac})/(2a) \tag{4.38}$$

First, if b^2 is much larger than $4ac$, then significance error arises in calculating the root of smaller magnitude, since $\sqrt{b^2 - 4ac} \simeq |b|$. It is therefore better to exploit the relationship

$$m_1 m_2 = c/a$$

and replace (4.38) by the formulae

$$\left.\begin{array}{l} m_1 = (-b + \sqrt{b^2 - 4ac})/(2a) \quad \text{if } b < 0 \\ m_1 = (-b - \sqrt{b^2 - 4ac})/(2a) \quad \text{if } b > 0 \\ m_2 = c/(am_1) \end{array}\right\} \tag{4.39}$$

Secondly, if $b^2 \simeq 4ac$, so that the roots m_1, m_2 are almost equal, then significance error occurs instead in the calculation of $\sqrt{b^2 - 4ac}$. Unfortunately there is no apparent remedy for this, other than to use higher (e.g. double) precision arithmetic. Indeed the problem is *ill conditioned* in this case.

Algorithm 4.3   General solution of $ay'' + by' + cy = 0$

Specify a, b, c and categorize into case (i), (ii), or (iii).
Determine the general solution in the form (4.32), with m_1, m_2, u, v (as required) determined from (4.31), but using (4.39) to calculate m_1, m_2 in place of (4.38).

Program 4.3   SECHOM: Homogeneous second order equations— general solution

```
LIST
SECHOM      1-JUN-1986 18:14

100      REM - SECHOM.BAS : Solution of Homogeneous Second Order
110      REM - Differential Equation with constant coefficients.
120      PRINT 'Equation of the form  AY'' + BY' + CY = 0'
130      PRINT 'Input coefficients A,B,C ';
140      INPUT A,B,C
150      GOSUB 220
160      REM - FLG denotes whether roots of quadratic are REAL or COMPLEX
170      REM -        (FLG = 0 REAL roots and FLG = 1 COMPLEX roots)
180      IF FLG = 0 AND M1 <> M2 THEN GOSUB 540
190      IF FLG = 0 AND M1 = M2 THEN GOSUB 580
200      IF FLG = 1 THEN GOSUB 620
210      GOTO 660
220      REM - Subroutine to solve the quadratic equation
230      REM -        A*X*X + 2*B1*X + C = 0   (B = 2*B1)
240      FLG = 0
250      IF A = 0 GOTO 510
260      B1 = .5 * B
270      D = B1 * B1 - A * C
280      IF D < 0 GOTO 390
290      REM - Real roots calculated
300      E = SQR(D)
310      IF B < 0 GOTO 340
320      M1 = (-B1-E)/A
330      GOTO 350
340      M1 = (-B1+E)/A
350      M2 = C/(A*M1)
360      PRINT 'Real roots'
370      PRINT 'M1,M2 = ';M1;',';M2
380      GOTO 530
390      REM - Complex conjugate roots calculated
400      FLG = 1
410      E = SQR(-D)
420      U1 = -B1/A
430      U2 = U1
440      V1 = E/A
450      V2 = -V1
460      PRINT 'Complex roots U+iV,U-iV'
470      PRINT 'REAL part U :',''IMAG part V :'
480      PRINT U1,V1
490      PRINT U2,V2
500      GOTO 530
510      PRINT 'Leading coefficient is zero'
520      PRINT ' equation is not quadratic '
530      RETURN
540      REM - Roots of quadratic are real and distinct
550      PRINT 'Solution is of the form :'
560      PRINT 'Y(x) = Aexp(';M1;'x) + Bexp(';M2;'x)'
570      RETURN
```

```
580    REM - Roots of quadratic are real and coincident
590    PRINT 'Solution is of the form :'
600    PRINT 'Y(x) = (A + Bx)exp('#M#'x)'
610    RETURN
620    REM - Roots of quadratic are complex conjugate pair
630    PRINT 'Solution is of the form :'
640    PRINT 'Y(x) = exp('#U1#'x)[Acos('#V1#'x) + Bsin('#V1#'x)]'
650    RETURN
660    END
```

Ready

Sample run 1

```
RUN
SECHOM

Equation of the form  AY'' + BY' + CY = 0
Input coefficients A,B,C ? 1,-3,2
Real roots
M1,M2 =  2 , 1
Solution is of the form :
Y(x) = Aexp( 2 x) + Bexp( 1 x)
Ready
```

Sample run 2

```
RUN
SECHOM

Equation of the form  AY'' + BY' + CY = 0
Input coefficients A,B,C ? 1,-6,9
Real roots
M1,M2 =  3 , 3
Solution is of the form :
Y(x) = (A + Bx)exp( 3 x)
Ready
```

Sample run 3

```
RUN
SECHOM

Equation of the form  AY'' + BY' + CY = 0
Input coefficients A,B,C ? 1,8,25
Complex roots U+iV,U-iV
REAL part U : IMAG part V :
 -4             3
 -4            -3
Solution is of the form :
Y(x) = exp(-4 x)[Acos( 3 x) + Bsin( 3 x)]
Ready
```

Program notes

(1) The subroutine to solve the auxiliary equation (4.30) is based on Program 3.8 in Reference 2, which was written for quadratic equations. (This implements (4.32), with (4.39) in place of (4.38).)

(2) The program uses four subroutines. The main subroutine on lines 230–530 solves a quadratic equation (as discussed in the previous note), and three subsidiary routines on lines 540–570, 580–610, 620–650 specify solutions corresponding to (4.32)(i), (ii), (iii) respectively.

(3) The three Sample runs test, respectively, the three types of solutions corresponding to (4.32)(i), (ii), (iii).

4.3.2 Particular integrals

By obtaining the general solution (4.32) of (4.21) in Programme 4.3 above, we have already determined the complementary function for the non-homogeneous equation (4.20), i.e.

$$ay'' + by' + cy = f(x) \tag{4.40}$$

It remains for us to determine a *particular integral* of this equation which can be added to the complementary function so as to give the general solution of (4.40). However, the only forms of forcing function $f(x)$ for which particular integrals are easily determined are the following ones:

$$f(x) = e^{rx} \tag{4.41}(i)$$

where r is real;

$$f(x) = e^{rx} \cos sx \text{ or } e^{rx} \sin sx \tag{4.41}(ii)$$

where r, s are real; and

$$f(x) = x^r \tag{4.41}(iii)$$

where r is an integer.

The details of solution are tricky for these general cases, and the reader who is unfamiliar with any mathematical methods for such differential equations may wish to rely on Program 4.4 below without reference to the details which now follow.

Writing $D \equiv d/dx$, we adopt the 'D operator' method for determining particular integrals (see Reference 1). In this approach (4.40) becomes

$$Q(D)y = (aD^2 + bD + c)y = f(x)$$

where

$$Q(m) = am^2 + bm + c$$

and we seek to evaluate

$$y = (aD^2 + bD + c)^{-1}f(x) = [Q(D)]^{-1}f(x)$$

by using binomial expansions and making the obvious deduction (for any function g)

$$D^{-1}g(x) \equiv \int g(x)\,dx \tag{4.42}$$

Two key results (Reference 1) are that, for any function F,

(a) $F(D)e^{mx} = F(m)e^{mx}$ if $F(m) \neq \infty$ (4.43)

(b) $F(D)[e^{mx}g(x)] = e^{mx}F(D+m)g(x)$ (4.44)

Now, from (4.43), (4.44) we deduce respectively that:

(a) *For* $f(x) = e^{mx}$, *where* $Q(m) \neq 0$ (*m real or complex*)

$$y = e^{mx}/Q(m)$$ (4.45)

(b) *For* $f(x)) = e^{mx}$, *where* $Q(m) = am^2 + bm + c = 0$,

$$y = [Q(D)]^{-1}e^{mx}1 = e^{mx}[Q(D+m)]^{-1}(1)$$
$$= e^{mx}[a(D+m)^2 + b(D+m) + c]^{-1}(1)$$
$$= e^{mx}[aD^2 + D(2am+b)]^{-1}(1)$$
$$= e^{mx}(2am+b)^{-1}[1 + a(2am+b)^{-1}D]^{-1}D^{-1}(1)$$
$$= e^{mx}(2am+b)^{-1}[1 - a(2am+b)^{-1}D + O(D^2)](x)$$

from (4.42)

i.e.

$$y = e^{mx}(2am+b)^{-1}[x - a(2am+b)^{-1}]$$ (4.46)

Now

$$e^{rx}(\cos sx + i \sin sx) = e^{(r+is)x}$$

and hence cases (4.41)(i), (ii) correspond to real and/or imaginary parts of e^{mx} for $m = r, r + is$. For $m = r$, the solutions (4.45), (4.46) give us particular integrals immediately:

(i) (a) *For* $f(x) = e^{rx}$ *where* $Q(r) \neq 0$,

$$y = (ar^2 + br + c)^{-1}e^{rx}$$ (4.47)

(b) *For* $f(x) = e^{rx}$ *where* $Q(r) = 0$,

$$y = w^{-1}e^{rx}(x - aw^{-1})$$ (4.48)

where

$$w = (2ar+b)^{-1}$$ (4.49)

For $m = r + is$,

$$Q(m) = a(r+is)^2 + b(r+is) + c = p + iq$$

where

$$p = a(r^2 - s^2) + br + c, \quad q = (2ar+b)s$$ (4.50)

and hence

$$[Q(m)]^{-1} = (p - iq)/(p^2 + q^2)$$ (4.51)

Thus

$$[Q(m)]^{-1} e^{mx} = \frac{p - iq}{p^2 + q^2} e^{rx}(\cos sx + i \sin sx) \qquad (4.52)$$

and taking real and imaginary parts in (4.45), (4.52):

(ii) (a) *For $f(x) = e^{rx} \cos sx$ or $e^{rx} \sin sx$ where $Q(r + is) \neq 0$,*

$$y = \frac{e^{rx}}{p^2 + q^2} (p \cos sx + q \sin sx) \qquad (4.53)$$

or

$$y = \frac{e^{rx}}{p^2 + q^2} (p \sin sx - q \cos sx) \qquad (4.54)$$

In the other case of (4.41)(ii) where $m = r + is$ and $Q(m) = 0$, from (4.46) we obtain immediately

$$y = e^{rx}(\cos sx + i \sin sx) \frac{p - iq}{p^2 + q^2} \left[x - \frac{a(p - iq)}{p^2 + q^2} \right]$$

where now $p = 2ar + b$, $q = 2as$. Note that either $p = 0$ (for $s \neq 0$) or $q = 0$ (for s = 0). On taking real and imaginary parts, and setting

$$t = 1/(p^2 + q^2) \qquad (4.55)$$

we obtain

(ii) (b) *For $f(x) = e^{rx} \cos sx$ or $e^{rx} \sin sx$ where $Q(r + is) = 0$,*

$$y = t e^{rx}[(p \cos sx + q \sin sx)(x - apt)$$
$$- aqt(p \sin sx - q \cos sx)] \qquad (4.56)$$

or

$$y = t e^{rx}[(p \sin sx - q \cos sx)(x - apt)$$
$$+ aqt(p \cos sx + q \sin sx)] \qquad (4.57)$$

Finally, we must consider case (iii), namely $f(x) = x^r$.

For simplicity take $r = 3$, and then the particular integral is given by

$$y = (aD^2 + bD + c)^{-1}x^3$$
$$= c^{-1}(1 + bc^{-1}D + ac^{-1}D^2)^{-1}x^3$$
$$= c^{-1}[1 - (bc^{-1}D + ac^{-1}D^2) + (bc^{-1}D + ac^{-1}D^2)^2$$
$$- (bc^{-1}D + ac^{-1}D^2)^3 + \dots]x^3$$

Noting that

$$1 \times x^3 = x^3, \quad Dx^3 = 3x^2, \quad D^2x^3 = 6x, \quad D^3x^3 = 6, \quad D^4x^3 = 0, \dots$$

we deduce, on ignoring terms in $D^4, D^5, \dots$, that:

(iii) *For* $f(x) = x^3$,

$$y = c^{-1}[x^3 - 3bc^{-1}x^2 + 6(ac^{-1} + b^2c^{-2})x^2$$
$$+ 6(2abc^{-2} - b^3c^{-3})] \tag{4.58}$$

All of the above results are combined in the following algorithm.

Algorithm 4.4A   Particular integrals of $ay'' + by' + c = f(x)$

(A) For $f(x) = e^{rx}$, where $r \neq m_1, m_2$ (roots of $Q(m) = am^2 + bm + c$) define y by (4.47).
For $f(x) = e^{rx}$, where $r = m_1$ or m_2, define y by (4.48).

(B) For $f(x) = e^{rx} \cos sx$, where $r = u$ and $|s| = |v|$ are *not both* true (i.e. $r + is$ is not $u \pm iv$, one of the roots of $Q(m)$) then define y by (4.53).
For $f(x) = e^{rx} \cos sx$, where $r = u$ and $|s|, = |v|$, define y by (4.56).

(C) For $f(x) = e^{rx} \sin sx$, $r = u$ and $|s| = |v|$ *not* both true, define y by (4.54).
For $f(x) = e^{rx} \sin sx$, $r = u$ and $|s| = |v|$, define y by (4.57).

(D) For $f(x) = x^3$, define y by (4.58).

Algorithm 4.4B   General solutions of $ay'' + by' + c = f(x)$

For cases (A), (B), (C), (D) of Algorithm 4.4A, add the particular integral to the corresponding complementary function of Algorithm 4.3.

The following program determines both complementary functions *and* particular solutions for Algorithm 4.4B.

Program 4.4   SECNON: Non-homogeneous second order
equations

```
LIST
SECNON

100    REM - SECNON.BAS : Solution of Non-Homogeneous Second Order
110    REM - Differential Equation with constant coefficients.
120    PRINT "Second Order Differential Equation of the form ";
130    PRINT "  AY'' + BY' + CY = F(X)"
140    PRINT "where F(X) = (A) exp(RX),(B) exp(RX)cos(SX),";
150    PRINT "(C) exp(RX)sin(SX),(D) X##3"
160    PRINT "Input coefficients A,B,C ";
170    INPUT A,B,C
180    GOSUB 380
190    REM - FLG denotes whether roots of quadratic are REAL or COMPLEX
200    REM -       (FLG = 0 REAL roots and FLG = 1 COMPLEX roots)
210    IF FLG = 0 AND M1 <> M2 THEN GOSUB 700
220    IF FLG = 0 AND M1 = M2 THEN GOSUB 740
230    IF FLG = 1 THEN GOSUB 780
240    PRINT
250    PRINT "Form of F(X) - "
260    PRINT "(A) F(X) = exp(RX)"
270    PRINT "(B) F(X) = exp(RX)cos(SX)"
280    PRINT "(C) F(X) = exp(RX)sin(SX)"
290    PRINT "(D) F(X) = X##3"
300    PRINT
```

```
310        PRINT 'Input A,B,C, or D ';
320        INPUT ANS$
330        IF ANS$ = 'A' THEN GOSUB 820
340        IF ANS$ = 'B' THEN GOSUB 930
350        IF ANS$ = 'C' THEN GOSUB 1120
360        IF ANS$ = 'D' THEN GOSUB 1300
370        GOTO 1350
380        REM - Subroutine to solve the quadratic equation
390        REM -      A*X*X + 2*B1*X + C = 0    (B = 2*B1)
400        FLG = 0
410        IF A = 0 GOTO 670
420        B1 = .5 * B
430        D = B1 * B1 - A * C
440        IF D < 0 GOTO 550
450        REM - Real roots calculated
460        E = SQR(D)
470        IF B < 0 GOTO 500
480        M1 = (-B1-E)/A
490        GOTO 510
500        M1 = (-B1+E)/A
510        M2 = C/(A*M1)
520        PRINT 'Real roots'
530        PRINT 'M1,M2 = ';M1;',';M2
540        GOTO 690
550        REM - Complex conjugate roots calculated
560        FLG = 1
570        E = SQR(-D)
580        U1 = -B1/A
590        U2 = U1
600        V1 = E/A
610        V2 = -V1
620        PRINT 'Complex roots U+iV,U-iV'
630        PRINT 'REAL part U :','IMAG part V :'
640        PRINT U1,V1
650        PRINT U2,V2
660        GOTO 690
670        PRINT 'Leading coefficient is zero'
680        PRINT ' equation is not quadratic '
690        .RETURN
700        REM - Roots of quadratic are real and distinct
710        PRINT 'Complementary Function :'
720        PRINT 'Y(x) = Aexp(';M1;'x) + Bexp(';M2;'x)'
730        RETURN
740        REM - Roots of quadratic are real and coincident
750        PRINT 'Complementary Function :'
760        PRINT 'Y(x) = (A + Bx)exp(';M1;'x)'
770        RETURN
780        REM - Roots of quadratic are complex conjugate pair
790        PRINT 'Complementary Function :'
800        PRINT 'Y(x) = exp(';U1;'x)[Acos(';V1;'x) + Bsin(';V1;'x)]'
810        RETURN
820        REM - F(X) = exp(RX)
830        PRINT 'Input R ';
840        INPUT R
850        DMTR = A*(R*R) + B*R + C
860        IF DMTR = 0 GOTO 900
870        PRINT 'Particular Integral : '
880        PRINT '[exp(';R;'x)]/[';DMTR;']'
890        GOTO 920
900        PRINT 'Particular Integral : '
910        PRINT '[';1/(2*A*R+B);'exp(';R;'x)][x-';A/(2*A*R+B);']'
920        RETURN
930        REM - F(X) = exp(RX)cos(SX)
940        PRINT 'Input R,S [S <> 0]';
950        INPUT R,S
960        IF FLG = 1 AND R=U1 AND ABS(S)=ABS(V1) GOTO 1030
970        P = A*((R*R)-(S*S))+B*R+C
980        Q = 2*A*R*S+B*S
990        PRINT 'Particular Integral : '
1000       PRINT 1/((P*P)+(Q*Q));'exp(';R;'x) [';P;'cos(';
1010       PRINT S;'x) + ';Q;'sin(';S;'x)]'
1020       GOTO 1110
1030       P = 2*A*R+B
1040       Q = 2*A*S
1050       PRINT 'Particular Integral : '
1060       PRINT 1/((P*P)+(Q*Q));'exp(';R;'x) [(';P;'cos(';
1070       PRINT S;'x) + ';Q;'sin(';S;'x)){x - ';
1080       PRINT A*P/((P*P)+(Q*Q));'} - ';
1090       PRINT A*Q/((P*P)+(Q*Q));'{';P;'sin(';S;
1100       PRINT 'x) - ';Q;'cos(';S;'x)}]'
1110       RETURN
```

```
1120    REM - F(X) = exp(RX)sin(SX)
1130    PRINT 'Input R,S [S <> 0]';
1140    INPUT R,S
1150    IF FLG = 1 AND R=U1 AND ABS(S)=ABS(V1) GOTO 1220
1160    P = A*((R*R)-(S*S))+B*R+C
1170    Q = 2*A*R*S+B*S
1180    PRINT 'Particular Integral : '
1190    PRINT 1/((P*P)+(Q*Q));'exp(';R;'x) [';P;'sin(';
1200    PRINT S;'x) - ';Q;'cos(';S;'x)]'
1210    GOTO 1290
1220    P = 2*A*R+B
1230    Q = 2*A*S
1240    PRINT 'Particular Integral : '
1250    PRINT 1/((P*P)+(Q*Q));'exp(';R;'x) [{';P;'sin(';
1260    PRINT S;'x) - ';Q;'cos(';S;'x)}(x - ';A*P/((P*P)+(Q*Q));
1270    PRINT '} + ';A*Q/((P*P)+(Q*Q));'{';P;'cos(';
1280    PRINT S;'x) + ';Q;'sin(';S;'x)}]'
1290    RETURN
1300    REM - F(X) = X**3
1310    PRINT 'Particular Integral : '
1320    PRINT '[';1/C;'x**3 + ';-3*B/(C*C);'x**2 + ';6/(C*C)*(B*B/C-A);
1330    PRINT 'x + ';6*B/(C*C*C)*(2*A-B*B/C);']'
1340    RETURN
1350    END
```

Ready

Sample run 1

```
RUN
SECNON

Second Order Differential Equation of the form    AY'' + BY' + CY = F(X)
where F(X) = (A) exp(RX),(B) exp(RX)cos(SX),(C) exp(RX)sin(SX),(D) X**3
Input coefficients A,B,C ? 1,-3,2
Real roots
M1,M2 =  2 , 1
Complementary Function :
Y(x) = Aexp( 2 x) + Bexp( 1 x)

Form of F(X) -
(A) F(X) = exp(RX)
(B) F(X) = exp(RX)cos(SX)
(C) F(X) = exp(RX)sin(SX)
(D) F(X) = X**3

Input A,B,C, or D ? A
Input R ? -2
Particular Integral :
[exp(-2 x)]/[ 12 ]
Ready
```

Sample run 2

```
RUN
SECNON

Second Order Differential Equation of the form    AY'' + BY' + CY = F(X)
where F(X) = (A) exp(RX),(B) exp(RX)cos(SX),(C) exp(RX)sin(SX),(D) X**3
Input coefficients A,B,C ? 1,-5,6
Real roots
M1,M2 =  3 , 2
Complementary Function :
Y(x) = Aexp( 3 x) + Bexp( 2 x)

Form of F(X) -
(A) F(X) = exp(RX)
(B) F(X) = exp(RX)cos(SX)
(C) F(X) = exp(RX)sin(SX)
(D) F(X) = X**3

Input A,B,C, or D ? A
Input R ? 2
Particular Integral :
[-1 exp( 2 x)][x--1 ]
Ready
```

Sample run 3

```
RUN
SECNON

Second Order Differential Equation of the form   AY'' + BY' + CY = F(X)
where F(X) = (A) exp(RX),(B) exp(RX)cos(SX),(C) exp(RX)sin(SX),(D) X**3
Input coefficients A,B,C ? 1,-2,1
Real roots
M1,M2 =   1 , 1
Complementary Function :
Y(x) = (A + Bx)exp( 1 x)

Form of F(X) -
(A) F(X) = exp(RX)
(B) F(X) = exp(RX)cos(SX)
(C) F(X) = exp(RX)sin(SX)
(D) F(X) = X**3

Input A,B,C, or D ? B
Input R,S [S <> 0]? 1,1
Particular Integral :
 1 exp( 1 x) [-1 cos( 1 x) +   0 sin( 1 x)]
Ready
```

Sample run 4

```
RUN
SECNON

Second Order Differential Equation of the form   AY'' + BY' + CY = F(X)
where F(X) = (A) exp(RX),(B) exp(RX)cos(SX),(C) exp(RX)sin(SX),(D) X**3
Input coefficients A,B,C ? 1,-4,13
Complex roots U+iV,U-iV
REAL part U : IMAG part V :
 2           3
 2          -3
Complementary Function :
Y(x) = exp( 2 x)[Acos( 3 x) + Bsin( 3 x)]

Form of F(X) -
(A) F(X) = exp(RX)
(B) F(X) = exp(RX)cos(SX)
(C) F(X) = exp(RX)sin(SX)
(D) F(X) = X**3

Input A,B,C, or D ? B
Input R,S [S <> 0]? 2,3
Particular Integral :
 .27777BE-01 exp( 2 x) [( 0 cos( 3 x) +   6 sin( 3 x))(x -   0 ) -   .166667 ( 0 si
n( 3 x) -   6 cos( 3 x))]
Ready
```

Sample run 5

```
RUN
SECNON

Second Order Differential Equation of the form   AY'' + BY' + CY = F(X)
where F(X) = (A) exp(RX),(B) exp(RX)cos(SX),(C) exp(RX)sin(SX),(D) X**3
Input coefficients A,B,C ? 1,-2,5
Complex roots U+iV,U-iV
REAL part U : IMAG part V :
 1           2
 1          -2
Complementary Function :
Y(x) = exp( 1 x)[Acos( 2 x) + Bsin( 2 x)]

Form of F(X) -
(A) F(X) = exp(RX)
(B) F(X) = exp(RX)cos(SX)
(C) F(X) = exp(RX)sin(SX)
(D) F(X) = X**3
```

```
Input A,B,C, or D ? C
Input R,S [S <> 0]? 1,2
Particular Integral :
 .0625 exp( 1 x) [{ 0 sin( 2 x) -  4 cos( 2 x)}(x - 0 } + .25 { 0 cos( 2 x) +
 4 sin( 2 x)}]
Ready
```

Sample run 6

```
RUN
SECNON

Second Order Differential Equation of the form   AY'' + BY' + CY = F(X)
where F(X) = (A) exp(RX),(B) exp(RX)cos(SX),(C) exp(RX)sin(SX),(D) X##3
Input coefficients A,B,C ? 1,-4,3
Real roots
M1,M2 =  3 , 1
Complementary Function :
Y(x) = Aexp( 3 x) + Bexp( 1 x)

Form of F(X) -
(A) F(X) = exp(RX)
(B) F(X) = exp(RX)cos(SX)
(C) F(X) = exp(RX)sin(SX)
(D) F(X) = X##3

Input A,B,C, or D ? C
Input R,S [S <> 0]? 1,1
Particular Integral :
 .2 exp( 1 x) [-1 sin( 1 x) - -2 cos( 1 x)]
Ready
```

Sample run 7

```
RUN
SECNON

Second Order Differential Equation of the form   AY'' + BY' + CY = F(X)
where F(X) = (A) exp(RX),(B) exp(RX)cos(SX),(C) exp(RX)sin(SX),(D) X##3
Input coefficients A,B,C ? 6,-5,1
Real roots
M1,M2 =  .5 , .333333
Complementary Function :
Y(x) = Aexp( .5 x) + Bexp( .333333 x)

Form of F(X) -
(A) F(X) = exp(RX)
(B) F(X) = exp(RX)cos(SX)
(C) F(X) = exp(RX)sin(SX)
(D) F(X) = X##3

Input A,B,C. or D ? D
Particular Integral :
[ 1 x##3 +  15 x##2 +  114 x +  390 ]
Ready
```

Program notes

(1) One subroutine 380–690 calculates the roots of the quadratic $Q(m)$. A flag FLG is set equal to 0 or 1 (during this subroutine) according as the solutions are real or complex.

(2) Three subroutines 700–730, 740–770, 780–810 determine the complementary functions corresponding respectively to real distinct, real coincident, and complex roots.

(3) Four subroutines 820–920, 930–1110, 1120–1290, 1300–1340 determine the particular integral corresponding to cases (A), (B), (C), (D) of Algorithm 4.4A.

(4) The sample runs test all seven distinct types of $f(x)$, as included in Algorithm 4.4A. (The three distinct cases for complementary functions were already tested in the sample runs of Program 4.3.)

4.4 Systems of second order constant-coefficient equations

We conclude with an elegant problem, which was already indirectly introduced in one of our earlier books, namely that of determining the unique solution of a system of simultaneous second order equations of the special 'simple harmonic motion' type that we considered in Section 4.3.1 above (problems (6.14)–(6.16) of Chapter 6 of Reference 3).

In mechanical systems with several (or indeed many) moving parts, the motion of any one part depends on the motion of the others. If the system is represented by a set of differential equations then each of the equations is likely to include *all* of the displacements of the separate pieces in some linear combination. In order to clarify the type of situation, consider the following pair of specific problems.

4.4.1 Problem (A)

A uniform light shaft of torsional rigidity μ, free to move in oiled bearings, carries three flywheels whose moments of inertia are I_1, I_2, I_3. The flywheels are spaced at distances l_1, l_2 apart (see *Figure 4.1*). Calculate the periods of free oscillation of the wheels about their mean position.

If θ_1, θ_2, θ_3 denote the angular deviations of the flywheels from their mean positions, then the equations of motion become

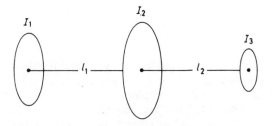

Figure 4.1. Rotationally oscillating flywheels.

$$I_1\ddot{\theta}_1 = -\frac{\mu}{l_1}(\theta_1 - \theta_2)$$

$$I_2\ddot{\theta}_2 = -\frac{\mu}{l_1}(\theta_2 - \theta_1) - \frac{\mu}{l_2}(\theta_2 - \theta_3) \qquad (4.59)$$

$$I_3\ddot{\theta}_3 = -\frac{\mu}{l_2}(\theta_3 - \theta_2)$$

A simple way of rewriting the equations (4.59) is to express them as a single vector differential equation

$$\mathbf{y''} + \mathbf{Ay} = \mathbf{0} \qquad (4.60)$$

where

$$\mathbf{y} = \begin{pmatrix} y_1 \\ y_2 \\ y_3 \end{pmatrix} = \begin{pmatrix} \theta_1 \\ \theta_2 \\ \theta_3 \end{pmatrix}$$

and

$$\mathbf{A} = \begin{pmatrix} k_1 & -k_1 & 0 \\ -k_2 & (k_2+k_3) & -k_3 \\ 0 & -k_4 & k_4 \end{pmatrix} \qquad (4.61)$$

with

$$k_1 = \mu/(I_1 l_1), \; k_2 = \mu/(I_2 l_1), \; k_3 = \mu/(I_2 l_2), \; k_4 = \mu/(I_3 l_2)$$

Here we have used 3×3 matrices and 3×1 vectors to reduce three simultaneous scalar equations (4.59) to one single matrix equation (4.60).

4.4.2 Problem (B)

Three particles of masses m_1, m_2, m_3 are joined in a straight line on a smooth horizontal plane by a pair of elastic strings of moduli λ_1, λ_2 and lengths l_1, l_2 (see *Figure 4.2*). Calculate the motions of the particles, based on their initial positions and velocities.

If y_1, y_2, y_3 denote the deviations of the three particles from their mean positions, then the equations of motion become

$$m_1\ddot{y}_1 = \lambda_1(y_2 - y_1)/l_1$$

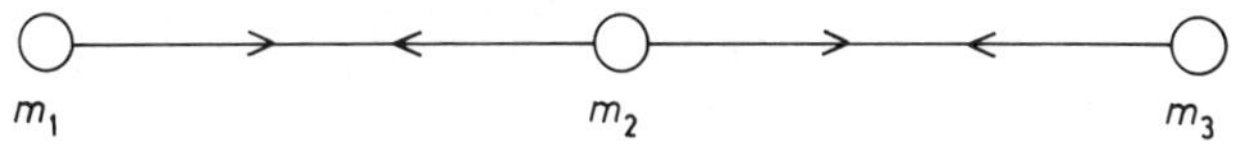

Figure 4.2.   Horizontally oscillating masses.

$$m_2\ddot{y}_2 = -\lambda_1(y_2 - y_1)/l_1 + \lambda_2(y_3 - y_2)/l_2 \qquad (4.62)$$

$$m_3\ddot{y}_3 = -\lambda_2(y_3 - y_2)/l_2$$

Once again, we may write this in the vector form (4.60) where

$$\mathbf{y} = (y_1 \; y_2 \; y_3)^{\mathrm{T}}$$

$$\mathbf{A} = \begin{pmatrix} K_1 & -K_1 & 0 \\ -K_2 & (K_2 + K_3) & -K_3 \\ 0 & -K_4 & K_4 \end{pmatrix} \qquad (4.63)$$

with

$$K_1 = \lambda_1/(l_1 m_1), \quad K_2 = \lambda_1/(l_1 m_2)$$
$$K_3 = \lambda_2/(l_2 m_2), \quad K_4 = \lambda_2/(l_2 m_3)$$

Note that Problem (A) above gives precisely the same matrix in the special case $k_1 = K_1$, $k_2 = K_2$, $k_3 = K_3$, $k_4 = K_4$.

Thus both Problems (A) and (B) lead to the vector equation (4.60), and the matrix $\mathbf{A}$ given by (4.61) is representative of both problems.

4.4.3 Method of solution of the vector differential equation

Now any 3×3 matrix $\mathbf{A}$ has a set of three eigenvalues $\lambda_1, \lambda_2, \lambda_3$ given by

$$|\mathbf{A} - \lambda\mathbf{I}| = 0 \qquad (4.64)$$

where

$$\mathbf{I} = \begin{pmatrix} 1 & 0 & 0 \\ 0 & 1 & 0 \\ 0 & 0 & 1 \end{pmatrix}$$

is the identity matrix, and a set of corresponding independent eigenvectors $\mathbf{x}_{(1)}, \mathbf{x}_{(2)}, \mathbf{x}_{(3)}$ which satisfy

$$(\mathbf{A} - \lambda\mathbf{I})\mathbf{x} = \mathbf{0} \quad (\lambda \text{ an eigenvalue}) \qquad (4.65)$$

Once $\lambda_1, \lambda_2, \lambda_3$ and $\mathbf{x}_{(1)}, \mathbf{x}_{(2)}, \mathbf{x}_{(3)}$ have been determined (see Reference 3 for a discussion of suitable methods), then (4.65) leads to the matrix equation

$$\mathbf{AK} = \mathbf{KD} \qquad (4.66)$$

where $\mathbf{K} = (\mathbf{x}_{(1)}|\mathbf{x}_{(2)}|\mathbf{x}_{(3)})$ is the matrix of eigenvectors and

$$\mathbf{D} = \begin{pmatrix} \lambda_1 & 0 & 0 \\ 0 & \lambda_2 & 0 \\ 0 & 0 & \lambda_3 \end{pmatrix}$$

is the diagonal matrix of eigenvalues.

For example, suppose that $k_1 = k_4 = 2$, and $k_2 = k_3 = 1$ in (4.61) above, so that

$$A = \begin{pmatrix} 2 & -2 & 0 \\ -1 & 2 & -1 \\ 0 & -2 & 2 \end{pmatrix} \qquad (4.67)$$

Then it is not difficult to deduce that

$$\lambda = \lambda_1, \lambda_2, \lambda_3 = 4, 2, 0$$

from (4.64) and

$$x = x_{(1)}, x_{(2)}, x_{(3)} = \begin{pmatrix} 1 \\ -1 \\ 1 \end{pmatrix}, \begin{pmatrix} 1 \\ 0 \\ -1 \end{pmatrix}, \begin{pmatrix} 1 \\ 1 \\ 1 \end{pmatrix}$$

from (4.65). [The reader is referred to Reference 3 for a discussion of eigenvalue problems.]

Hence (4.66) follows with

$$K = \begin{pmatrix} 1 & 1 & 1 \\ -1 & 0 & 1 \\ 1 & -1 & 1 \end{pmatrix} \text{ and } D = \begin{pmatrix} 4 & 0 & 0 \\ 0 & 2 & 0 \\ 0 & 0 & 0 \end{pmatrix} \qquad (4.68)$$

It remains to exploit this information in order to simplify (4.60)

Now, suppose that we make a change of variables from $y = (y_1 y_2 y_3)^T$ to $z = (z_1\ z_2\ z_3)^T$, by writing

$$y = Kz \qquad (4.69)$$

For example, for the matrix A given by (4.67), this would give

$$\begin{pmatrix} y_1 \\ y_2 \\ y_3 \end{pmatrix} = \begin{pmatrix} 1 & 1 & 1 \\ -1 & 0 & 1 \\ 1 & -1 & 1 \end{pmatrix} \begin{pmatrix} z_1 \\ z_2 \\ z_3 \end{pmatrix}$$

i.e.

$$y_1 = z_1 + z_2 + z_3$$
$$y_2 = -z_1 + z_3 \qquad (4.70)$$
$$y_3 = z_1 - z_2 + z_3$$

Then, from (4.69), the original system (4.60) of differential equations becomes

$$Kz'' + AKz = 0$$

From (4.66) it follows that

$$\mathbf{Kz''} + \mathbf{KDz} = \mathbf{K}(\mathbf{z''} + \mathbf{Dz}) = 0$$

Since the eigenvectors are independent $\mathbf{K}$ is non-singular (i.e. $|\mathbf{K}| \neq 0$), and hence we may pre-multiply by $\mathbf{K}^{-1}$ in the last equation to obtain

$$\mathbf{z''} + \mathbf{Dz} = 0 \tag{4.71a}$$

i.e.

$$
\begin{aligned}
z_1'' + \lambda_1 z_1 &= 0 \\
z_2'' + \lambda_2 z_2 &= 0 \\
z_3'' + \lambda_3 z_3 &= 0
\end{aligned}
\tag{4.71b}
$$

The resulting system (4.7.1) is an 'uncoupled' system of differential equations (i.e. each equation in (4.71b) involves only one of the dependent variables z_1, z_2, z_3) and it is precisely of the special form (4.33) considered in Program 4.2.

The general solution of (4.71) is defined by (4.35), (4.34) depending on whether $\lambda_1, \lambda_2, \lambda_3$ are negative, zero, or positive. For example for the specific problem and matrix (4.67) ($\lambda_1 = 4$, $\lambda_2 = 2$, $\lambda_3 = 0$) we obtain

$$
\begin{aligned}
z_1 &= A_1 \cos 2t + B_1 \sin 2t \\
z_2 &= A_2 \cos \sqrt{2} t + B_2 \sin \sqrt{2} t \\
z_3 &= A_3 + B_3 t
\end{aligned}
\tag{4.72}
$$

The three pairs of arbitrary constants ($A_1, B_1; A_2, B_2; A_3, B_3$, say) in z_1, z_2, z_3 are determined by specifying appropriate boundary conditions, such as

$$
\mathbf{y}(0) = \mathbf{a} = \begin{pmatrix} a_1 \\ a_2 \\ a_3 \end{pmatrix}, \quad \mathbf{y}'(0) = \mathbf{b} = \begin{pmatrix} b_1 \\ b_2 \\ b_3 \end{pmatrix}
$$

where $a_1, a_2, a_3, b_1, b_2, b_3$ are given constants. (This would correspond to the system being initiated with velocity $\mathbf{b}$ from the position $\mathbf{a}$.) Then (4.69) gives

$$
\left.
\begin{aligned}
\mathbf{Kz}(0) &= \mathbf{a} \\
\mathbf{Kz}'(0) &= \mathbf{b}
\end{aligned}
\right\}
\tag{4.73}
$$

Now, suppose that $\mathbf{z}(0) = \boldsymbol{\alpha}$ and $\mathbf{z}'(0) = \boldsymbol{\beta}$. Then

$$\mathbf{K}\boldsymbol{\alpha} = \mathbf{a}$$

$$\mathbf{K}\boldsymbol{\beta} = \mathbf{b} \tag{4.74}$$

Hence $\boldsymbol{\alpha}$, $\boldsymbol{\beta} = \mathbf{z}(0)$, $\mathbf{z}'(0)$ are determined *uniquely* by solving the pair of *linear algebraic systems* (4.74).

We now have a pair of initial conditions

$$\mathbf{z}(0) = \boldsymbol{\alpha}, \ \mathbf{z}'(0) = \boldsymbol{\beta} \tag{4.75}$$

which are sufficient to determine uniquely the solution of the uncoupled system (4.71).

For example, in the specific example (4.65), if the initial conditions are

$$\mathbf{y}(0) = \mathbf{a} = (0 \quad 0 \quad 0)^{\mathrm{T}}, \ \mathbf{y}'(0) = \mathbf{b} = (1 \ -2 \ -1)^{\mathrm{T}}$$

Then (4.74) gives $\boldsymbol{\alpha} = \mathbf{0}$ and

$$\begin{pmatrix} 1 & 1 & 1 \\ -1 & 0 & 1 \\ 1 & -1 & 1 \end{pmatrix} \begin{pmatrix} \beta_1 \\ \beta_2 \\ \beta_3 \end{pmatrix} = \begin{pmatrix} 1 \\ -2 \\ -1 \end{pmatrix}$$

from which we may deduce that

$$(\beta_1 \quad \beta_2 \quad \beta_3)^{\mathrm{T}} = (1 \quad 1 \ -1)^{\mathrm{T}}$$

Now the initial conditions (4.75) applied to the general solution (4.72) immediately give

$$z_1 = \frac{1}{2}\sin 2t, \quad z_2 = \frac{1}{\sqrt{2}}\sin\sqrt{2}t, \quad z_3 = -t \tag{4.76}$$

Hence the solution has been determined in the $\mathbf{z}$ variables.

To complete the solution of the problems, we should express it in terms of the original variables $\mathbf{y}$ (i.e. y_1, y_2, y_3), and this is immediately possible on substituting $\mathbf{y} = \mathbf{K}\mathbf{z}$ (from 4.67). Thus, for (4.76), the final solution becomes

$$\mathbf{y} = \begin{pmatrix} y_1 \\ y_2 \\ y_3 \end{pmatrix} = \begin{pmatrix} 1 & 1 & 1 \\ -1 & 0 & 1 \\ 1 & -1 & 1 \end{pmatrix} \begin{pmatrix} z_1 \\ z_2 \\ z_3 \end{pmatrix} = \begin{pmatrix} \frac{1}{2}\sin 2t + \frac{1}{\sqrt{2}}\sin\sqrt{2}t - t \\ -\frac{1}{2}\sin 2t - t \\ \frac{1}{2}\sin 2t - \frac{1}{\sqrt{2}}\sin\sqrt{2}t - t \end{pmatrix}$$

4.4.4 A numerical algorithm

The above method is immediately applicable to the problem of uncoupling and solving a system of three simultaneous equations of the general form

$$\mathbf{y}'' + \mathbf{A}\mathbf{y} = \begin{pmatrix} y_1 \\ y_2 \\ y_3 \end{pmatrix}'' + \begin{pmatrix} a_{11} & a_{12} & a_{13} \\ a_{21} & a_{22} & a_{23} \\ a_{31} & a_{32} & a_{33} \end{pmatrix} \begin{pmatrix} y_1 \\ y_2 \\ y_3 \end{pmatrix} = 0$$

where $\mathbf{A}$ is a specified (general) matrix. The details are summarized below in Algorithm 4.5. Note that two particular subroutines are required (in steps 2 and 3, respectively):

  (i) the determination of all eigenvalues and eigenvectors of $\mathbf{A}$
  (ii) the solution of a system of simultaneous linear equations

It is suggested that (i) may be readily achieved for a 3×3 problem, by adopting the power method to obtain two eigenvalues (Programs 6.5, 6.6A of Reference 3) and using the relation

$$\lambda_1 + \lambda_2 + \lambda_3 = a_{11} + a_{22} + a_{33} \tag{4.77}$$

to obtain the third eigenvalue.

For a higher order problem, a more powerful algorithm such as the QR method might be adopted.

The solution of (ii) may be obtained by Gauss elimination (Program 5.4A of Reference 3).

Algorithm 4.5 Solution of $\mathbf{y}'' + \mathbf{A}\mathbf{y} = \mathbf{0}$; $\mathbf{y}(0) = \mathbf{a}$, $\mathbf{y}'(0) = \mathbf{b}$

  (1) Specify the matrix $\mathbf{A}$, and the initial displacement $\mathbf{a}$ and velocity $\mathbf{b}$.
  (2) Determine all eigenvalues and corresponding independent eigenvectors of $\mathbf{A}$, and hence define $\mathbf{K}$ and $\mathbf{D}$ by (4.64) (e.g. by Program 6.6A of Reference 3).
  (3) Solve the two algebraic systems (4.74) for $\boldsymbol{\alpha}$, $\boldsymbol{\beta}$ (e.g. by Program 5.4A of Reference 3).
  (4) Solve $\mathbf{z}'' + \mathbf{D}\mathbf{z} = \mathbf{0}$; $\mathbf{z}(0) = \boldsymbol{\alpha}$, $\mathbf{z}'(0) = \boldsymbol{\beta}$ (by Program 4.2 above).
  (5) The solution of the problem is $\mathbf{y} = \mathbf{K}\mathbf{z}$.

No complete computer program for Algorithm 4.5 is presented here, although the reader may wish to write one as an exercise. However, any specific 3×3 problem may readily be solved by calling upon the three component programs 6.6A, 5.4A (Reference 3) and 4.2 (this book), while carrying out the instructions of Algorithm 4.5.

4.5 References

1. LAMBE, G.G. and TRANTER, C.J., *Differential Equations for Engineers and Scientists*, The English Universities Press Ltd, London (1961)
2. MASON, J.C., *BASIC Numerical Mathematics*, Butterworths (1983)
3. MASON, J.C., *BASIC Matrix Methods*, Butterworths (1984)

PROBLEMS

(4.1) Classify each of the following differential equations as either linear or non-linear, and state its order:

(i) $y''' + yy'' = 0$,   (ii) $y' = 1 + y^2$,   (iii) $xy'' + y = x^3$.

(4.2) Attempt the solution of the following differential equations by using an integrating factor. In which problem(s) is it not possible to use standard analytical methods of integration?

(i) $(\tan x)y' + y = x$,   (ii) $y' - 2xy = x$
(iii) $x^2 y' - y = x^2 \exp(-1/x)$,   (iv) $xy' + y = \exp(1/x)$

(4.3) Derive the general solutions (4.16) of the equation

$$y' + \lambda y = f(x) \tag{*}$$

for the three choices (4.13) of $f(x)$.
  Obtain in addition the general solution of (*) for
(a) $f(x) = e^{rx} \cos sx$, (b) $f(x) = e^{rx} \sin sx$.
[Take real and imaginary parts of $f(x) = \exp((r + is)x)$.]

(4.4) Use Program 4.1 to solve (i) $y' + y = 0$, (ii) $y' + y = e^x$, (iii) $y' + 25y = e^{-5x}$, (iv) $y' - y = \sin 2x$.

(4.5) The current i in an electrical circuit, with inductance L, resistance R and electromotive force e, is given by

$$L\frac{di}{dt} + Ri = e$$

If $e = E \cos \omega t$ and $i = 0$ at time $t = 0$, use Algorithm 4.1 to determine the explicit solution for i in terms of L, R, E, ω. What is the solution if $L = R = E = \omega = 1$ unit?

(4.6) Derive the general solutions (4.32), (4.31) of the equation

$$ay'' + by' + cy = 0 \tag{**}$$

[In case (ii), assume $y = g(x)\exp(m_1 x)$.]

(4.7) Write down the solutions of the following initial-value problems (using (4.34), (4.35)):

   (i) $y'' + 9y = 0$; $y(0) = 0$, $y'(0) = 2$
   (ii) $y'' - 16y = 0$; $y(0) = 1$, $y'(0) = 0$
   (iii) $y'' = 0$; $y(0) = 1$, $y'(0) = 2$

Test Program 4.2 on these problems.

(4.8) Modify Program 4.2 so that it solves the *boundary-value* problem

$$y'' + \lambda y = 0; \quad y(x_0) = y_0, \quad y(x_1) = y_1$$

where $\lambda, x_0, y_0, x_1, y_1$ are given.

   Test this new program on the problems

   (i) $y'' + 9y = 0$; $y(0) = 0$, $y(\pi/2) = 1$
   (ii) $y'' - 16y = 0$; $y(0) = 2$, $y(0.1) = \exp(0.4) + \exp(-0.4)$
   (iii) $y'' = 0$; $y(0) = 1$, $y(1) = 2$

(4.9) Write down the general solutions of the following equations:

   (i) $3y'' + 5y' - 2y = 0$,   (ii) $4y'' - 4y' + y = 0$,
   (iii) $y'' + 2y' + 2y = 0$

Test Program 4.3 on these problems.

(4.10) A horizontal spring–dashpot system, in which the motion of a mass m is controlled by a spring of modulus k and a dashpot of constant c, satisfies the equation of motion

$$m\ddot{y} = -c\dot{y} - ky$$

Using Program 4.3, determine the explicit solution $y(t)$ for all t, given that

$$m = 1000 \text{ kg}, \quad k = 10\,000 \text{ N m}^{-1}, \quad c = 4000 \text{ Ns m}^{-1}$$

(4.11) The angular displacement θ of a car fuel gauge needle is given by

$$\ddot{\theta} + 2G\omega_N\dot{\theta} + \omega_N^2\theta = 0$$

subject to

$$\dot{\theta} = 0, \quad \theta = \theta_{ss} \quad \text{at } t = 0$$

where G is the damping ratio, ω_N is the natural frequency, and θ_{ss} is the steady state angular displacement.

   Using Program 4.3, determine the general solution of the differential equation, and hence deduce the explicit form of the unique solution of the problem in terms of θ_{ss}, given that

$$G = 2.0, \quad \omega_N = 11 \text{ rad s}^{-1}$$

(4.12) Extend Program 4.3 to include the specification of initial conditions

$$y(0)=y_0, \quad y'(0)=d_0$$

and the determination of the unique solution y for these conditions. Test the new program on the problem

$$y'' - 2y' + y = 0; \quad y(0) = 1, \quad y'(0) = 2$$

[Solution: $y = (1 + x)e^x$]

(4.13) Determine (by hand) particular integrals of the equations

   (i) $3y'' + 5y' - 2y = e^x$,   (ii) $3y'' + 5y' - 2y = e^{-2x}$
  (iii) $y'' + 2y' + 2y = e^{-x} \cos 2x$,   (iv) $y'' + 2y' + 2y = e^{-x} \sin x$
   (v) $4y'' - 4y' + y = x^3$
Test Program 4.4 on these problems.

(4.14) An electrical circuit with inductance L, resistance R and a condenser of capacitance C is connected to an electromotive force $e = E \sin \omega t$, thus giving the equation for the current i:

$$L\frac{d^2 i}{dt^2} + R\frac{di}{dt} + \frac{i}{C} = \omega E \cos \omega t$$

Find the steady state current (i.e. the *particular integral* of the equation) at time t after the circuit is closed for the following cases:
   (i) $L=1$, $R=1$, $C=1$, $\omega=1$
  (ii) $L=1$, $R=2$, $C=1$, $\omega=1$
  (iii) $L=1$, $R=3$, $C=1$, $\omega=1$

(4.15) Extend Program 4.4, so that a unique solution is determined to the problem for the case

$$f(x) = x^3$$

corresponding to specified initial conditions

$$y(0) = y_0, \quad y'(0) = d_0$$

Test this new program on the problem

$$4y'' - 4y' + y = x^3; \quad y(0) = 1, \quad y'(0) = 3$$

(4.16) Solve by Algorithm 4.5 the coupled systems of equations:
  (i) $y_1'' + 3y_1 - 3y_2 = 0; \; y_1(0) = 0, \; y_1'(0) = 1$
     $y_2'' - 2y_1 + 4y_2 - 2y_3 = 0; \; y_2(0) = 0, \; y_2'(0) = 2$
     $y_3'' - 2y_2 + 2y_3 = 0; \; y_3(0) = 0, \; y_3'(0) = 1$

i.e. Problem (B) of Section 4.4.2 with $K_1 = 3$, $K_2 = K_3 = 2$, $K_4 = 2$.

(ii) $y_1'' + y_1 - y_2 = 0$; $y_1(0) = 1$, $y_1'(0) = 0$
$\quad\quad y_2'' - 2y_1 + 5y_2 - 3y_3 = 0$; $y_2(0) = 1$, $y_2'(0) = 0$
$\quad\quad y_3'' - 4y_2 + 4y_3 = 0$; $y_3(0) = 1$, $y_3'(0) = 0$
Hint: The solution of $z'' + \omega^2 z = 0$; $z(0) = \alpha$, $z'(0) = 0$ is $z = \alpha \cos \omega t$.

(4.17) Write a computer program to implement Algorithm 4.5 for a general 3×3 matrix $\mathbf{A}$ (with positive or zero eigenvalues), and test the program on the systems of Problem (4.15).

Chapter 5

Initial-value problems

ESSENTIAL THEORY

In the previous chapter we looked at certain linear differential equations and were able to determine analytical techniques for solving them. However, although we solved important classes of problems, the differential equations were very special ones, and it is appropriate that we now move to problems of greater generality and breadth.

A general first order differential equation for an initial-value problem is given in the form

$$y' = f(x, y), \quad y(x_0) = C \tag{5.1}$$

Here x_0 and C are specified constants, and $f(x,y)$ is some specified function of both x and y. For example, particular specifications of $f(x,y)$, x_0 and C might be

(i) $f(x,y) = y$, $x_0 = 0$, $C = 1$,   (ii) $f(x,y) = 1 + y^2$, $x_0 = 0$, $C = 0$
(iii) $f(x, y) = 1 - 2xy$, $x_0 = 0$, $C = 0$

The unique solutions of (5.1) corresponding to these three cases are

(i) $y = e^x$,   (ii) $y = \tan x$
(iii) $y = e^{-x^2} \int_0^x e^{t^2} \, dt$

In general it is necessary to use a numerical method to solve (5.1), and the style of such a method is as follows. Once y is known at any particular point x, then the gradient of y is known there by (5.1), and it is hence possible to estimate y at a neighbouring point $x + h$. This process may then be repeated over and over again, at successive steps of h, to estimate y at $x + h$, $x + 2h$, $x + 3h$, ... Of course we need an initial value of y from which to start this process, and that is where the initial condition $y(x_0) = C$ comes in. The simplest method of this type is Euler's method.

5.1 Euler's method

We recall from our discussion of finite differences in Chapter 3, and in particular from (3.26), that

$$y'(x_i) = y_i' = h^{-1}(y_{i+1} - y_i) + O(h) \tag{5.2}$$

where

$$y_i = y(x_i) \quad \text{and} \quad x_i = x_0 + ih$$

Applying the differential equation (5.1) at the value $x = x_i$,

$$y'_i = h^{-1}(y_{i+1} - y_i) + O(h) = f(x_i, y_i)$$

Thus

$$y_{i+1} = y_i + hf(x_i, y_i) + O(h^2)$$

If we neglect the term $O(h^2)$, which (for h small) is smaller than the other terms, then we obtain the numerical approximation

$$y_{i+1} = y_i + hf(x_i, y_i) \quad (i = 0, 1, 2, \ldots) \qquad (5.3)$$

The neglected term $O(h^2)$ is in fact the *truncation error* in (5.3).

This formula (5.3) enables us to calculate y_1, then y_2, and so on. Since the solution is obtained directly from (5.3), (5.3) is termed an *explicit method*. Specifically, if we use the simplified notation

$$f_i = f(x_i, y_i)$$

then the algorithm is as follows.

Algorithm 5.1 Euler's method

Specify x_0 and h to determine stations $x_i = x_0 + ih$ $(i = 1, 2, \ldots)$.
Specify the number n of steps to be adopted.
Specify the function $f(x, y)$ and the initial value $y_0 = C$.
Calculate $y_{i+1} := y_i + hf_i$ $(i = 0, 1, 2, \ldots, N-1)$.

Throughout this book we shall describe a method as of order k if the error in calculating y_{i+1} from y_i has an error $O(h^{k+1})$. Thus the computed y_{i+1} has an expansion in powers of h which agrees with that of the true y_{i+1} up to and including the term in h^k.

Since Euler's method, given by (5.3), is correct in powers of h only up to the first power, it is termed a *first order method*.

The above derivation of Euler's method is an algebraic one and has the advantage of simultaneously providing the form of the truncation error. However, there is a very simple geometric way of viewing Euler's method and this is shown in *Figure 5.1*. Let $P_0, P_1, P_2, \ldots,$ $P_i, P_{i+1}, \ldots$ denote the points (x_0, y_0), (x_1, y_1), (x_2, y_2), $\ldots,$ $(x_i, y_i), (x_{i+1}, y_{i+1}) \ldots$ on the graph of the solution (y against x). Then, if x_i and y_i are known (and also P_i is known), the gradient y'_i of the graph at P_i is given by the differential equation as

$$y'_i = f(x_i, y_i) = f_i$$

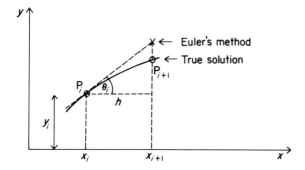

Figure 5.1. Euler's method.

If it is assumed that the step h is so small that the graph from P_i to P_{i+1} (unknown) may be taken to be a straight line, then it is clear from Figure 5.1 that

$$y_{i+1} = y_i + h \tan \theta_i = y_i + hy_i' = y_i + hf_i$$

Hence y_{i+1} is then precisely defined by Euler's method. Thus Euler's method views the solution as a set of straight lines joined together (technically called a 'piecewise linear function'), with the gradients of each individual line given by the differential equation at its left end point.

5.1.1 Example of Euler's method

For example, consider the initial-value problem

$$y' = x + y, \quad y(0) = 1 \tag{5.4}$$

for which the true solution is

$$y = 2 e^x - (1 + x) \tag{5.5}$$

Here $f(x, y) = x + y$, $C = 1$, and let us choose $h = 0.1$. Then Algorithm 5.1 progresses as follows.

Stations: $x_0 = 0$, $x_i = 0.1$, $x_2 = 0.2$, ...

$$\begin{aligned}
y(0.1) = y_1 &= y_0 + hf_0 = y_0 + h(x_0 + y_0) \\
&= 1 + 0.1(0 + 1) = 1.1 \\
y(0.2) = y_2 &= y_1 + hf_1 = y_1 + h(x_1 + y_1) \\
&= 1.1 + 0.1(0.1 + 1.1) = 1.22
\end{aligned}$$

$$y(0.3) = y_3 = y_2 + hf_2 = y_2 + h(x_2 + y_2)$$
$$= 1.22 + 0.1(0.2 + 1.22) = 1.362$$

etc.

By way of comparison, the true solutions (5.5) of (5.4) are $y(0.1) = 1.110$, $y(0.2) = 1.243$, $y(0.3) = 1.400$. The program for Algorithm 5.1 now follows. We have not developed this program to any degree of sophistication, since it is a slow algorithm and inappropriate for harder problems.

Program 5.1 EULER: Euler's method for first order equations

```
10 REM- EULER: EULER'S METHOD FOR
20 REM- Y'=F(X,Y) , Y(X0)=Y0
30 REM- FIXED STEP H
40 DEF FNF(X,Y)=Y
50 PRINT "STEP-LENGTH";
60 INPUT H
70 PRINT "INITIAL VALUES X0,Y0";
80 INPUT X0,Y0
90 PRINT "NO OF STEPS";
100 INPUT N
110 PRINT "        X:","   Y:"
120 PRINT X0;"        ";Y0
130 FOR I=0 TO N-1
140 Y1=Y0+H*FNF(X0,Y0)
150 X0=X0+H
160 Y0=Y1
170 PRINT X0;"        ";Y0
180 NEXT I
190 END
>
```

Sample run 1

```
RUN
STEP-LENGTH?.01
INITIAL VALUES X0,Y0?0,1
NO OF STEPS?10
     X:        Y:
      0         1
    1E-2      1.01
    2E-2      1.0201
    3E-2      1.030301
    4E-2      1.04060401
    5E-2      1.05101005
    6E-2      1.06152015
    7E-2      1.07213535
    8E-2      1.08285671
    9E-2      1.09368527
    0.1       1.10462213
>
```

Sample run 2

```
>40 DEF FNF(X,Y)=1-2*X*Y
>RUN
STEP-LENGTH?.01
INITIAL VALUES X0,Y0?0,1
NO OF STEPS?10
     X:        Y:
      0         1
    1E-2      1.01
    2E-2      1.019798
    3E-2      1.02939008
    4E-2      1.03877245
    5E-2      1.04794143
    6E-2      1.05689349
    7E-2      1.06562521
    8E-2      1.07413334
    9E-2      1.08241473
    0.1       1.09046638
>
```

Program notes

(1) The suffices 1 and 0 have been used in place of suffices $i+1$ and i in Algorithm 5.1, since this saves using subscripted variables.

(2) The program is at present set up for the problem

$$y' = y, \quad y(0) = 1$$

i.e.

$$f(x, y) = y \quad \text{and} \quad y_0 = 1$$

The differential equation can be changed by redefining $f(x,y)$ in the DEF statement 40. This is carried out in Sample run 2.

(3) The true solution for Sample run 1 is $y = e^x$, giving $y(0.1) = 1.10517$, and hence the computed $y(0.1)$ is correct to three decimal places.

In Sample run 2, with $f(x, y) = 1 - 2xy$, we obtained $y(0.1) \simeq 1.0905$. When the calculation was repeated with 1000 steps, the more accurate value $y(0.1) = 1.08940$ was obtained. Thus 10 steps yielded nearly three decimal places.

5.1.2 Truncation error in Euler's method

In the case of

$$y' = y, \quad y(0) = 1 \qquad (5.6)$$

where the true solution is $y = e^x$, suppose N steps of h are used to reach the point $x = X = x_N = Nh$ from the point $x = x_0 = 0$. Then

$$y(X) = y_N, \quad Nh = X, \quad \text{and so } h = X/N$$

Here

$$y_{i+1} = y_i + hf_i = y_i + hy_i$$

since $f(x,y) = y$. Thus Euler's (approximate) method gives

$$y_{i+1} = (1 + h)y_i \qquad (5.7)$$

If (5.7) is applied successively to y_0 for $i = 0,1 \ldots, N$, then it is clear that

$$y_N = (1 + h)^N y_0 = (1 + X/N)^N$$

Now as $N \to \infty$, it is well known (from the definition of e) that $(1 + X/N)^N$ approaches e^X. Hence for h sufficiently small (i.e. $N = 1/h$ sufficiently large) Euler's method can be made to solve (5.6) as accurately as we may require.

We can also compare the approximate formula (5.7) linking y_{i+1} to

y_i with the true formula in the case of this problem. In this case, since $x_i = ih$, the true solutions are

$$y_i = e^{x_i} = e^{ih} \quad \text{and} \quad y_{i+1} = e^{(i+1)h}$$

Hence

$$y_{i+1} = e^h y_i$$

Now

$$e^h = 1 + h + \frac{h^2}{2!} + \frac{h^3}{3!} + \dots$$

Hence

$$y_{i+1} = \left(1 + h + \frac{h^2}{2} + \frac{h^3}{6} + \dots\right) y_i \tag{5.8}$$

and so the true relation is

$$y_{i+1} = [1 + h + O(h^2)] y_i$$

This confirms that the *'local' truncation error* is proportional to h^2. We use the adjective 'local', because we are only considering the error in moving from $x = x_i$ to $x = x_{i+1} = x_i + h$.

However, if we wish to compute y_N at $x = X = x_n$ then we must accumulate $N = X/h$ local truncation errors, and so the resulting *global truncation error* must surely be proportional to h. Specifically the true y_N is given by

$$y_N = [1 + h + O(h^2)]^N y_0$$
$$= [(1+h)^N + N(1+h)^{N-1} O(h^2) + \dots] y_0$$

Now, for some constant A,

$$N(1+h)^{N-1} O(h^2) \simeq N(1+h)^{N-1} A h^2$$
$$= (1+h)^{N-1} A X h$$
$$= O(h)$$

Hence

$$y_N = [(1+h)^N + O(h)] y_0 \tag{5.9}$$

and the global truncation error in Euler's method (5.7) is indeed $O(h)$.

Thus the error in calculating a solution of an initial-value problem at a general point $x = X$ should be seen as being proportional to the step h. In practice this means that a very large number of small steps must be taken, say of the order of 10 000 steps to achieve an accuracy of about 0.0001 at any general point. Clearly we must look for faster methods than this.

5.2 Simple predictor–corrector methods

There are two main types of numerical method for solving initial-value problems, namely 'predictor–corrector' and 'Runge–Kutta' methods, and we shall use Euler's method (above) as a stepping-stone to these methods.

Now Euler's method might be viewed as a crude method of integration. If we assume that $f(x, y)$ is constant and equal to f_i $= f(x_i, y_i)$ along the solution curve from $P_i : (x_i, y_i)$ to $P_{i+1} : (x_{i+1}, y_{i+1})$, then by integration

$$y' = f(x,y), \quad y(0) = y_0$$

implies that

$$y_{i+1} - y_i = \int_{x_i}^{x_{i+1}} f(x, y(x)) \, dx \simeq \int_{x_i}^{x_{i+1}} f(x_i, y(x_i)) \, dx$$

$$= \int_{x_i}^{x_{i+1}} f_i \, dx = f_i \left[x \right]_{x_i}^{x_{i+1}}$$

$$= h f_i$$

This is indeed Euler's method.

However, we know, from our study of numerical integration in Reference 1, a simple but rather better method of integration than this, namely the trapezium rule. Using this approach,

$$y_{i+1} - y_i = \int_{x_i}^{x_{i+1}} f(x, y(x)) \, dx$$

$$\simeq \frac{h}{2} [f(x_i, y(x_i)) + f(x_{i+1}, y(x_{i+1}))]$$

$$= \frac{h}{2} [f(x_i, y_i) + f(x_{i+1}, y_{i+1})] = \frac{h}{2} (f_i + f_{i+1})$$

We deduce the trapezium rule approximation

$$y_{i+1} = y_i + \tfrac{1}{2} h [f(x_i, y_i) + f(x_{i+1}, y_{i+1})] \tag{5.10}$$

for calculating y_{i+1} from x_i and y_i.

Unfortunately there is something 'fishy' about this formula at the moment. For f_{i+1} on the right-hand side depends on the value of y_{i+1}, which is unknown, and so the left-hand side cannot be evaluated. Such a formula is termed an *implicit method*. However, we are not lost, since we can obtain an estimate $\hat{y}_{i+1}$ for y_{i+1} by applying the simpler Euler's method first. Thus we combine (5.3) and (5.10) to obtain

$$\hat{y}_{i+1} = y_i + hf(x_i, y_i) \tag{5.11a}$$

$$y_{i+1} = y_i + \tfrac{1}{2}h[f(x_i, y_i) + f(x_{i+1}, \hat{y}_{i+1})] \tag{5.11b}$$

where $y_0 = y(x_0) = C$.

This pair of formulae may be used at each step (from x_i to x_{i+1}) of the process, which is then called a *predictor–corrector* method. Euler's method (5.11a) is termed the *predictor* (since it provides a first estimate $\hat{y}_{i+1}$ of y_{i+1}) and the trapezium rule (5.11b) is termed the *corrector* (since it improves on the value $\hat{y}_{i+1}$).

5.2.1 Example of Euler–trapezium rule

Consider again the example of Section 5.1.1, namely

$$y' = x + y, \quad y(0) = 1$$

with $h = 0.1$. Then the predictor–corrector method progresses as follows:

Stations: $x_0 = 0$, $x_1 = 0.1$, $x_2 = 0.2, \ldots$

$$\hat{y}_1 = y_0 + hf(x_0, y_0) = y_0 + h(x_0 + y_0) = 1 + 0.1(0 + 1) = 1.1$$

$$y(0.1) = y_1 = y_0 + \frac{h}{2}[f(x_0, y_0) + f(x_1, y_1)]$$

$$= y_0 + \frac{h}{2}[(x_0 + y_0) + (x_1 + y_1)]$$

$$= 1 + 0.05\,[(0 + 1) + (0.1 + 1.1)]$$

$$= 1.11$$

$$\hat{y}_2 = y_1 + hf(x_1, y_1) = y_1 + h(x_1 + y_1)$$
$$= 1.11 + 0.1(0.1 + 1.11) = 1.231$$

$$y(0.2) = y_2 = y_1 + \frac{h}{2}[f(x_1, y_1) + f(x_2, \hat{y}_2)]$$

$$= y_1 + \frac{h}{2}[(x_1 + y_1) + (x_2 + \hat{y}_2)]$$

$$= 1.11 + 0.05\,[(0.1 + 1.11) + (0.2 + 1.231)]$$

$$= 1.11 + 0.05(2.641) = 1.11 + 0.13205 = 1.24205$$

etc.

The true solutions (5.5), for comparison, are

$$y(0.1) = 1.1103, \quad y(0.2) = 1.2428$$

and we note that we have obtained substantially more accurate results than were obtained by Euler's method in Section 5.1.1.

5.2.2 Fundamental Euler–trapezium algorithm and program

The algorithm that includes (5.11) is formalized below and followed by the corresponding program.

Algorithm 5.2 Fundamental Euler–trapezium method

Specify x_0 and h and determine stations $x_i = x_0 + ih$.
Specify the function $f(x, y)$ and the initial value $y_0 = C$.
Calculate $y_{i+1}(i = 0, 1, 2, \ldots, N-1)$ from the pair of formulae (5.11).

Program 5.2 EULTRAP: Fundamental Euler–trapezium method

```
LIST
    10REM- EULTRAP: EULER-TRAPEZIUM
    20REM- METHOD FOR Y'=F(X,Y),Y(X0)=C.
    30REM- SINGLE CORRECTOR PER STEP
    40DEF FNF(X,Y)=Y
    50INPUT "STEP LENGTH H";
    60INPUT H
    70PRINT "INITIAL VALUES X0,Y0";
    80INPUT X0,Y0
    90PRINT "NO OF STEPS N";
    100INPUT N
    110PRINT "        X:","    Y:"
    120PRINT X0;"    ";Y0
    130FOR I=0 TO N-1
    140Y1=Y0+H*FNF(X0,Y0)
    150X1=X0+H
    160Y1=Y0+.5*H*(FNF(X0,Y0)+FNF(X1,Y1))
    170PRINT X1;"    ";Y1
    180X0=X1
    190Y0=Y1
    200NEXT I
    210END
>
```

Sample run 1

```
RUN
STEP LENGTH H?.01
INITIAL VALUES X0,Y0?0,1
NO OF STEPS N?10
        X:        Y:
        0         1
      1E-2    1.01005
      2E-2    1.020201
      3E-2    1.03045402
      4E-2    1.04081009
      5E-2    1.05127023
      6E-2    1.06183549
      7E-2    1.07250694
      8E-2    1.08328563
      9E-2    1.09417266
      0.1     1.10516909
>
```

Sample run 2

```
40      DEF FNF(X,Y)=1-2*X*Y
>RUN
STEP LENGTH H?.01
INITIAL VALUES X0,Y0?0,1
NO OF STEPS N?10
        X:        Y:
        0         1
      1E-2    1.009899
      2E-2    1.01959407
      3E-2    1.0290811
      4E-2    1.03835729
      5E-2    1.04741818
      6E-2    1.05626065
      7E-2    1.0648814
      8E-2    1.07327727
      9E-2    1.08144524
      0.1     1.08938244
>.
```

Program notes

(1) In the program it is not necessary to use different symbols for $\hat{y}_{i+1}$ and y_{i+1}. In fact the superscript $\hat{\ }$ becomes superfluous, and the two simpler assignment statements replace the mathematical statements (5.11a), (5.11b).

(2) Variables Y1 and Y0 are used to story y_{i+1} and y_i for all i.

(3) In Sample run 1 the true solution would be $y(1) = 1.105171$ and so the computed $y(1)$ is correct to five decimal places at least.

(4) In Sample run 2 we have solved $y' = 1 - 2xy$. Here $y(0.1)$ is in error by 0.00002, whereas Program 5.1 gave an error of 0.001. This is consistent with an error of $O(h^3)$ compared with that of $O(h^2)$ in Euler's method.

5.2.3 Euler–trapezium method with multiple correctors

In the predictor–corrector method of Algorithm 5.2, the value y_{i+1} of y at x_{i+1} is determined from y_i by one prediction (5.11a) and one correction (5.11b). However, there is no reason why we should not make a second correction by evaluating (5.11b) with the value of y_{i+1} obtained from the first corrector replacing $\hat{y}_{i+1}$ on the right-hand side. Similarly we may make a third correction, a fourth correction, etc. In practice it is rarely necessary or worthwhile to use more than two or three corrections. The mathematical expressions for the process are as follows:

Predictor: $\hat{y}_{i+1} = y_i + hf(x_i, y_i)$ $\qquad$ (5.12)

1st Corrector: $y^*_{i+1} = y_i + \frac{1}{2}h[f(x_i, y_i) + f(x_{i+1}, \hat{y}_{i+1})]$ ⎫

2nd Corrector: $y^{**}_{i+1} = y_i + \frac{1}{2}h[f(x_i, y_i) + f(x_{i+1}, y^*_{i+1})]$ ⎬ (5.13)

3rd Corrector: $y^{***}_{i+1} = y_i + \frac{1}{2}h[f(x_i, y_i) + f(x_{i+1}, y^{**}_{i+1})]$ ⎭

etc.

In fact all the superscripts $\hat{\ }$, $*$, $**$, etc. may be deleted if the equals sign is replaced by the assignment $(:=)$, and this is expressed as an algorithm as follows.

Algorithm 5.3 Euler–trapezium method with p corrections/step

Define x_0, the step h, the number of steps n, the initial value y_0, and the function $f(x, y)$.
Carry out the following assignments in order (for $i = 0, 1, \ldots, n-1$)

$y_{i+1} := y_i + hf(x_i, y_i)$ $\qquad$ (once)

$y_{i+1} := y_i + \frac{1}{2}h[f(x_i, y_i) + f(x_{i+1}, y_{i+1})]$ $\qquad$ (p times)

Consider again the example (compare Sections 5.1.1, 5.2.1)

$$y' = x + y, \quad y(0) = 1 \quad \text{with } h = 0.1$$

Then Algorithm 5.3 progresses as follows, with $x_0 = 0$, $x_1 = 0.1$, $x_2 = 0.2, \ldots$:

$$\hat{y}_1 = y_0 + h(x_0 + y_0) = 1 + 0.1(0 + 1) = 1.1$$

$$y_1^* = y_0 + \tfrac{1}{2}h[(x_0 + y_0) + (x_1 + \hat{y}_1)] = 1.11$$

$$y_1^{**} = y_0 + \tfrac{1}{2}h[(x_0 + y_0) + (x_1 + y_1^*)] = 1 + 0.05[(0 + 1) + (0.1 + 1.11)]$$
$$= 1.1105$$

$$y_1^{***} = y_0 + \tfrac{1}{2}h[(x_0 + y_0) + (x_1 + y_1^{**})] = 1.1105(25)$$

Clearly the values are converging to 1.1105 ..., whereas the true solution is 1.1103. The first corrected value y_1^* ($= 1.11$) is substantially more accurate than the predicted value $\hat{y}_1$ ($= 1.1$), but the second corrected value y_1^{**} ($= 1.1105$) gives only a marginal improvement over y_1^*.

The following program makes a further simple adjustment to Algorithm 5.3, so as to provide considerable added flexibility. First, values x_0, h, n and p are input and solutions $y(x_0), \ldots, y(x_n)$ are obtained; then, if required, a new value of x_0 is chosen equal to the previous x_n and a new h, n, p are input, and solutions $y(x_0), \ldots, y(x_n)$ are obtained at the new points; and so on. For example, we might first input $x_0 = 0$, $h = 0.01$, $n = 10$, $p = 2$ and determine $y(0), y(0.01), \ldots, y(0.1)$. Then we might set $x_0 = 0.1$ ($= $ old x_n), input $h = 0.02$, $n = 10$, $p = 3$ and determine $y(0.1)$, $y(0.12), \ldots, y(0.3)$; and so on. Effectively, we thus allow variable steps and variable numbers of correctors in the numerical solution.

Program 5.3   EUTRMUL: Euler–trapezium with p (multiple) correctors/step

```
LIST
  10REM- EUTRMUL: EULER-TRAPEZIUM
  20REM- METHOD FOR Y'=F(X,Y),Y(X0)=Y0
  30REM- P (MULTIPLE) CORRECTORS/STEP
  40REM- NUMBER N OF STEPS H IS
  50REM- PERFORMED, AND THEN FURTHER
  60REM- SETS OF STEPS MAY BE TAKEN
  70REM- WITH NEW X0= LAST X.
  80REM- F(X,Y) DEFINED BY FNF(X,Y).
  90DEF FNF(X,Y)=X+Y
 100PRINT "1ST X, 1ST Y";
 110INPUT X0,Y0
 120PRINT "NO OF STEPS, STEP LENGTH"
 130INPUT N,H
 140PRINT "NO OF CORRECTORS / STEP";
 150INPUT P
 160PRINT "   X","  PRED Y","   CORR Y"
 170PRINT X0," ";Y0," ";Y0
 180FOR I=0 TO N-1
```

```
190X1=X0+H
200F=FNF(X0,Y0)
210Y1=Y0+H*F
220PRINT X1," ";Y1
230IF P=0 THEN 280
240FOR J=1 TO P
250Y1=Y0+.5*H*(F+FNF(X1,Y1))
260PRINT X1," ","   ";Y1
270NEXT J
280X0=X1
290Y0=Y1
300NEXT I
310REM- RESTART WITH NEW X0=LAST X
320PRINT "TYPE 1 TO TERMINATE"
330PRINT "TYPE 0 FOR NEW X0=LAST X"
340INPUT FLAG
350IF FLAG=0  THEN 120
360END
>
```

Sample run

```
272     YY=EXP(X1)-X1-1
>274    PRINT "TRUE:",YY
>RUN
1ST X, 1ST Y?0,0
NO OF STEPS, STEP LENGTH
?5,.01
NO OF CORRECTORS / STEP?3
    X       PRED Y       CORR Y
        0 0              0
      1E-2 0
      1E-2               5E-5
      1E-2               5.025E-5
      1E-2               5.025125E-5
TRUE:    5.01670875E-5
      2E-2 1.50753762E-4
      2E-2               2.01256275E-4
      2E-2               2.01508788E-4
      2E-2               2.0151005E-4
TRUE:    2.01339833E-4
      3E-2 4.03525151E-4
      3E-2               4.54535226E-4
      3E-2               4.54790276E-4
      3E-2               4.54791552E-4
TRUE:    4.54534311E-4
      4E-2 7.59339467E-4
      4E-2               8.10862207E-4
      4E-2               8.1111982E-4
      4E-2               8.11121108E-4
TRUE:    8.10774043E-4
      5E-2 1.21923232E-3
      5E-2               1.27127288E-3
      5E-2               1.27153308E-3
      5E-2               1.27153438E-3
TRUE:    1.27109652E-3
TYPE 1 TO TERMINATE
TYPE 0 FOR NEW X0=LAST X
?0
NO OF STEPS, STEP LENGTH
?2,.025
NO OF CORRECTORS / STEP?2
    X       PRED Y       CORR Y
      5E-2 1.27153438E-3            1.27153438E-3
      7.5E-2 2.55332274E-3
      7.5E-2             2.88184509E-3
      7.5E-2             2.88595162E-3
TRUE:    2.88415048E-3
      0.1 4.83310041E-3
      0.1               5.16993977E-3
      0.1               5.17415026E-3
TRUE:    5.17091807E-3
TYPE 1 TO TERMINATE
TYPE 0 FOR NEW X0=LAST X
?1
>
```

Program notes

(1) In the sample run, the true solution is

$$y = e^x - x - 1$$

and the computed solutions have been compared with the true solution by including the statements 272 and 274.
(2) Note, from the sample run, that the corrected values are converging at each step, but that they are not converging to the true solution. They are in fact converging to the solution y_{i+1} of the equation (5.10) above, namely the value corresponding to a *true* trapezium rule in which the *same* y_{i+1} appears on both left and right of equation (5.10). (However, the true trapezium rule does not yield the exact solution, of course.)

5.2.4 The truncation error in the Euler–trapezium method

We saw above that Euler's method was a first order method, which calculated y_{i+1} from y_i with a local truncation error of $O(h^2)$, and we must now determine the error in the presumably more accurate Euler–trapezium predictor–corrector method.

5.2.4.1 *Euler–trapezium with one correction*
Consider the simple Euler–trapezium method (5.11) in which just one correction is carried out. Then, combining the pair of formulae (5.11), we obtain

$$y_{i+1}^C = y_i + \tfrac{1}{2}h[f(x_i, y_i) + f(x_i + h, y_i + k)] \tag{5.14}$$

where $k = hf(x_i, y_i) = hf_i$, and the superscript C denotes the computed value.

Now a two-variable Taylor series expansion takes the form

$$f(x_i + h, y_i + k) = f(x_i, y_i) + (hf_x + kf_y)_i + \frac{1}{2!}(h^2 f_{xx} + 2hk f_{xy} + k^2 f_{yy})_i$$
$$+ \dots$$

where f_x denotes $\partial f/\partial x$, $(f_x)_i$ is the value of f_x at (x_i, y_i), etc. It follows from (5.14) that

$$y_{i+1}^C = y_i + \tfrac{1}{2}h[f_i + f_i + (hf_x + hff_y)_i + \frac{1}{2!}(h^2 f_{xx} + 2h^2 f_{xy} + h^2 f^2 f_{yy})_i$$
$$+ \dots]$$

i.e.

$$y_{i+1}^C = y_i + hf_i + \tfrac{1}{2}h^2(f_x + ff_y)_i + O(h^3) \tag{5.15}$$

Now the true value of y_{i+1} is given by

$$y_{i+1} = y(x_i + h) = y_i + hy_i' + \frac{h^2}{2!}y_i'' + \ldots$$

$$= y_i + hf_i + \frac{h^2}{2!}(f_x + ff_y)_i + O(h^3) \tag{5.16}$$

From (5.15) and (5.16) we immediately deduce that

$$y_{i+1}^C = y_{i+1} + O(h^3) \tag{5.17}$$

Thus the Euler–trapezium single correction is a *second order method* and has a local truncation error of $O(h^3)$, clearly superior to that of Euler's method.

5.2.4.2 *Euler–trapezium with multiple corrections*
Let us now assume that the method is applied with a sufficient number of corrections, say m, for convergence to be obtained to the true trapezium rule (5.10). Then

$$y_{i+1}^C = y_i + \frac{h}{2}[f(x_i, y_i) + f(x_{i+1}, y_{i+1}^C)] \tag{5.18}$$

However, the true value is given by

$$y_{i+1} = y_i + hy_i' + \frac{h^2}{2!}y_i'' + O(h^3) \tag{5.19}$$

Also

$$y_i = y(x_{i+1} - h) = y(x_{i+1}) - hy'(x_{i+1}) + \frac{h^2}{2!}y''(x_{i+1}) + O(h^3)$$

i.e.

$$y_i = y_{i+1} - hy_{i+1}' + \frac{h^2}{2!}y_{i+1}'' + O(h^3) \tag{5.20}$$

Subtracting (5.20) from (5.19), we deduce that

$$y_{i+1} - y_i = -(y_{i+1} - y_i) + h(y_i' + y_{i+1}') - \frac{h^2}{2}(y_{i+1}'' - y_i'') + O(h^3)$$

Thus

$$y_{i+1} - y_i = \frac{h}{2}(y_i' + y_{i+1}') - \frac{h^2}{4}[y''(x_i + h) - y''(x_i)] + O(h^3)$$

Now

$$y''(x_i + h) = y''(x_i) + hy'''(x_i) + O(h^2)$$

and

$$y_i', y'_{i+1} = f_i, f_{i+1}$$

Hence

$$y_{i+1} = y_i + \frac{h}{2}(f_i + f_{i+1}) + O(h^3) \tag{5.21}$$

Thus the true trapezium rule (5.18) has a local truncation error of $O(h^3)$ and the Euler–trapezium rule with multiple corrections is a *second order (predictor–corrector) method*.

This seems surprising at first sight, since we do not appear to have obtained more accuracy by multiple corrections than we did by a single correction (as in (5.17)). However, the error in (5.18) is in fact significantly smaller than the error in (5.17). Although both errors are proportional to h^3, the constant of proportionality is different. This is confirmed in the following example.

5.2.4.3 *Example:* $y' = y$
Consider the specific example

$$y' = f(x, y) = y, \quad y(0) = 1 \tag{5.22}$$

Then one correction, as in (5.14), gives

$$y^C_{i+1} = y_i + \tfrac{1}{2}h(y_i + \hat{y}_{i+1}), \quad \text{where } \hat{y}_{i+1} = y_i + hy_i$$

Thus

$$y^C_{i+1} = y_i + \tfrac{1}{2}h(y_i + y_i + hy_i) = \left(1 + h + \frac{h^2}{2}\right)y_i \tag{5.23}$$

Now the true solution is $y = e^x$ and so

$$y_{i+1} = e^h y_i = \left(1 + h + \frac{h^2}{2} + \frac{h^3}{6} + \ldots\right)y_i \tag{5.24}$$

and by comparing (5.23) and (5.24) we deduce that

$$y^C_{i+1} = y_{i+1} - \frac{h^3}{6}y_i + O(h^4) \tag{5.25}$$

The local truncation error is thus approximately $-\tfrac{1}{6}h^3 y_i$.

However if *two* corrections are performed, then

$$y_{i+1}^{C} = y_i + \tfrac{1}{2}h\left[y_i + \left(1 + h + \frac{h^2}{2}\right)y_i\right]$$

i.e.

$$y_{i+1}^{C} = \left(1 + h + \frac{h^2}{2} + \frac{h^3}{4}\right)y_i \tag{5.26}$$

By comparing (5.26) and (5.24) we obtain

$$y_{i+1}^{C} = y_{i+1} + \frac{h^3}{12}y_i + O(h^4) \tag{5.27}$$

Clearly, comparing (5.27) and (5.25), the truncation error for two corrections is approximately half that for one correction, although both errors are $O(h^3)$.

5.3 Euler–trapezium method for second order differential equations

Consider the second order differential equation

$$y'' = g(x, y, y') \tag{5.28}$$

subject to the initial conditions

$$y(x_0) = C, \, y'(x_0) = D \tag{5.29}$$

where g is some function of the three variables x, y, y'. Here 'acceleration' is explicitly known by a formula involving 'time', 'displacement' and 'velocity' (using the terminology of dynamics).

Introduce a new variable z, where $z = y'$ (so that in the case of a dynamics problem the velocity is the new variable). Then (5.28), (5.29) may immediately be rewritten as the pair of simultaneous first order differential equations

$$y' = z \tag{5.30a}$$

$$z' = g(x, y, z) \tag{5.30b}$$

subject to the initial conditions

$$y(x_0) = C, \quad z(x_0) = D \tag{5.31}$$

We may now extend the methods developed above in a natural way by using vectors. Let us denote $z(x_i)$, namely the value of $z = y'$ at the station x_i, by z_i, and let us define vectors (columns with two components):

$$\mathbf{y} = \begin{pmatrix} y \\ z \end{pmatrix}, \quad \mathbf{f}(x, \mathbf{y}) = \mathbf{f}(x, y, z) = \begin{pmatrix} z \\ g(x, y, z) \end{pmatrix}$$

$$\mathbf{C} = \begin{pmatrix} C \\ D \end{pmatrix}, \quad \mathbf{y}_i = \begin{pmatrix} y_i \\ z_i \end{pmatrix} \quad \text{etc.} \tag{5.32}$$

Then (5.30), (5.31) take the form

$$\mathbf{y}' = \mathbf{f}(x, \mathbf{y}), \quad \mathbf{y}(x_0) = \mathbf{C} \tag{5.33}$$

and the Euler–trapezium rule with one correction becomes

$$\hat{\mathbf{y}}_{i+1} = \mathbf{y}_i + h\mathbf{f}(x_i, \mathbf{y}_i) \tag{5.34a}$$

$$\mathbf{y}_{i+1} = \mathbf{y}_i + \tfrac{1}{2}h[\mathbf{f}(x_i, \mathbf{y}_i) + \mathbf{f}(x_{i+1}, \hat{\mathbf{y}}_{i+1})] \tag{5.34b}$$

This is precisely the same as (5.11) above, but with y and f in bold type to become vectors! Rewriting this in scalar form, using (5.32), we obtain the following algorithm.

Algorithm 5.4A. Euler–trapezium with one correction—second order equation

Define x_0, the step h, the number of steps n, the initial values $y_0 = C$ and $z_0 = y_0' = D$, and the function $g(x, y, z)$.
Calculate y_{i+1}, z_{i+1} $(i = 0, 1, \ldots, n-1)$ from

$$\hat{y}_{i+1} = y_i + hz_i, \quad \hat{z}_{i+1} = z_i + hg(x_i, y_i, z_i) \tag{5.35}$$

$$y_{i+1} = y_i + \tfrac{1}{2}h(z_i + \hat{z}_{i+1}) \tag{5.36a}$$

$$z_{i+1} = z_i + \tfrac{1}{2}h[g(x_i, y_i, z_i) + g(x_{i+1}, \hat{y}_{i+1}, \hat{z}_{i+1})] \tag{5.36b}$$

Note that we have neither used assignments ($:=$) nor removed the superscripts $\hat{}$. If we do so, then the algorithm is altered, since $\hat{y}_{i+1}$ in (5.36b) is then defined by (5.36a) instead of (5.35). (This does not make too much difference in practice, but it does technically change the algorithm.)

The algorithm is readily generalized as follows to permit m corrections, by defining $y_{i+1}^{(1)}, y_{i+1}^{(2)}, \ldots, y_{i+1}^{(m)}$ to be the first, second, $\ldots$, mth corrected y values, etc. (This replaces the 'unprogrammable' notation $y_{i+1}^*, y_{i+1}^{**}, y_{i+1}^{***}, \ldots$)

Algorithm 5.4B. Euler–trapezium with repeated corrections— second order equation

Define x_0, step h, number of steps n, number of corrections m,

initial values $y_0 = C$ and $z_0 = D$, and function $g(x, y, z)$.
Calculate $y_{i+1}, z_{i+1} = y_{i+1}^{(m)}, z_{i+1}^{(m)}$ $(i = 0, \ldots, n-1)$ from

$$y_{i+1}^{(0)} = y_i + hz_i, \quad z_{i+1}^{(0)} = z_i + hg(x_i, y_i, z_i) \tag{5.37}$$

For $k = 1, 2, \ldots, m$:

$$y_{i+1}^{(k)} = y_i + \tfrac{1}{2}h[z_i + z_{i+1}^{(k-1)}] \tag{5.38a}$$

$$z_{i+1}^{(k)} = z_i + \tfrac{1}{2}h[g(x_i, y_i, z_i) + g(x_{i+1}, y_{i+1}^{(k-1)}, z_{i+1}^{(k-1)})] \tag{5.38b}$$

5.3.1 Examples of problems

At first sight the second order equation (5.28) may look forbidding in
its generality. However, it enables us to deal with a wide variety of
problems and is in practice very convenient to program by using a
DEF statement for the function g.

Consider, for example, the equation

$$y'' - 2y' + y = x \tag{5.39}$$

which has the general solution (see Chapter 4)

$$y = (A + Bx)e^x + (x + 2) \tag{5.40}$$

[The first term, the complementary function, corresponds to the
double root $m = 1$ of the auxiliary equation $m^2 - 2m + 1 = 0$. The
second term is the particular integral.] Equation (5.39) is rewritten

$$y'' = g(x, y, y') = x - y + 2y'$$

Thus

$$g(x, y, z) = x - y + 2z \tag{5.41}$$

5.3.2. BASIC program

The program corresponding to Algorithm (5.4A) now follows, and
the example (5.39), based on the function (5.41), is used for the first
problem.

Program 5.4 EUTRSEC: Euler–trapezium for second order
equations

```
     LIST
10REM- EUTRSEC: EULER TRAPEZIUM
20REM- METHOD FOR SECOND ORDER EQN
30REM- Y'' =G(X,Y,Y'), Y(X0)=Y0 AND
40REM- Y'(X0)=Y'0.  -BASED ON THE
50REM- PAIR OF SIMULTANEOUS EQNS
60REM- Y'=Z, Z'=G(X,Y,Z) WITH
70REM- Y(X0)=Y0 AND Z(X0)=Z0=Y'0.
80REM- P CORRECTORS/FIXED STEP H.
90REM- NUMBER N OF STEPS H IS
```

```
100REM- PERFORMED, AND THEN FURTHER
110REM- SETS OF STEPS MAY BE TAKEN
120REM- WITH NEW X0= LAST X.
130REM- G(X,Y,Z) DEFINED BY FNG:
140DEF FNG(X,Y,Z)=X-Y+2*Z
150PRINT "1ST X, 1ST Y, 1ST Y'"
160INPUT X0,Y0,Z0
170PRINT "NO OF STEPS, STEP LENGTH"
180INPUT N,H
190PRINT "NO OF CORRECTORS/STEP";
200INPUT P
210PRINT"X"," ";"1ST Y"," ";"1ST Y'"
220PRINT X0;" ";Y0;" ";Z0
230FOR I=1 TO N
240X1=X0+H
250G=FNG(X0,Y0,Z0)
260Y1=Y0+H*Z0
270Z1=Z0+H*G
280PRINT"X"," ";"PRE Y"," ";"PRE Y'"
290PRINT X1;" ";Y1;" ";Z1
300IF P=0 THEN 380
310PRINT"X"," ";"COR Y"," ";"COR Y'"
320FOR J=1 TO P
330YY1=Y1
340Y1=Y0+.5*H*(Z0+Z1)
350Z1=Z0+.5*H*(G+FNG(X1,YY1,Z1))
360PRINT X1;" ";Y1;" ";Z1
370NEXT J
380X0=X1
390Y0=Y1
400Z0=Z1
410NEXT I
420REM- CONTINUE WITH NEW X0=LAST X
430PRINT "TYPE 1 TO TERMINATE"
440PRINT "TYPE 0 FOR NEW X0=LAST X"
450INPUT FLAG
460IF FLAG=0 THEN 170
470END
>
```

Sample run

```
RUN
1ST X, 1ST Y, 1ST Y'
?0,2,2
NO OF STEPS, STEP LENGTH
?5,.01
NO OF CORRECTORS/STEP?2
X          1ST Y        1ST Y'
           0 2 2
X          PRE Y        PRE Y'
           1E-2 2.02 2.02
X          COR Y        COR Y'
           1E-2 2.0201 2.02015
           1E-2 2.02010075 2.020151
X          PRE Y        PRE Y'
           2E-2 2.04030226 2.04045301
X          COR Y        COR Y'
           2E-2 2.04040377 2.04060502
           2E-2 2.04040453 2.04060604
X          PRE Y        PRE Y'
           3E-2 2.06081059 2.06121411
X          COR Y        COR Y'
           3E-2 2.06091363 2.06136816
           3E-2 2.0609144 2.06136919
X          PRE Y        PRE Y'
           4E-2 2.08152809 2.08228743
X          COR Y        COR Y'
           4E-2 2.08163268 2.08244354
           4E-2 2.08163346 2.08244458
X          PRE Y        PRE Y'
           5E-2 2.10245791 2.10367714
X          COR Y        COR Y'
           5E-2 2.10256407 2.10383534
           5E-2 2.10256486 2.10383639
TYPE 1 TO TERMINATE
```

```
TYPE 0 FOR NEW X0=LAST X
?0
NO OF STEPS, STEP LENGTH
?2,.025
NO OF CORRECTORS/STEP?1
X          1ST Y        1ST Y'
           5E-2 2.10256486 2.10383639
X          PRE Y        PRE Y'
           7.5E-2 2.15516077 2.15771409
X          COR Y        COR Y'
           7.5E-2 2.15583424 2.15871608
X          PRE Y        PRE Y'
           0.1 2.20980215 2.21463103
X          COR Y        COR Y'
           0.1 2.21050108 2.21566681
TYPE 1 TO TERMINATE
TYPE 0 FOR NEW X0=LAST X
?1
>
```

Program notes

(1) X0,Y0,Z0 and X1,Y1,Z1 are used for x_i, y_i, z_i and $x_{i+1}, y_{i+1}, z_{i+1}$ throughout.

(2) The defined function FNG(X,Y,Z) is used for $g(x, y, z)$.

(3) YY1 is used to store $\hat{y}_{i+1}$ (i.e. Y1) in line 330 (for use later in line 350) since Y1 is changed in line 340.

(4) The program is set up for the equation

$$y'' = g(x, y, y') = x - y + 2y'$$

In the sample run, this is solved for $y(0) = 2$, $y'(0) = 2$, and the corresponding true solution is then

$$y = xe^x + x + 2, \quad y' = (x+1)e^x + 1$$

Thus $y(0.1) = 2.210517$, $y'(0.1) = 2.215688$ and both have been calculated within 0.00002.

5.4 Runge–Kutta methods

We return now for the remainder of this chapter to the first order equation

$$y' = f(x, y), \quad y(x_0) = y_0 = C$$

In Section 5.2.4.1, we noted that the simple Euler–trapezium rule (with one correction) could be written (by (5.14)) as a single formula

$$y^C_{i+1} = y_i + \tfrac{1}{2}h[f(x_i, y_i) + f(x_i + h, y_i + hf_i)] \tag{5.42}$$

and we showed that its expansion (by (5.15)) reproduced the Taylor series for the true y_{i+1} up to terms in h^2, namely

$$y_{i+1} = y_i + hf_i + \tfrac{1}{2}h^2(f_x + ff_y)_i + O(h^3)$$

Here y^C_{i+1} is used to denote the calculated (approximate) value and y_{i+1} to denote the true value.

Now (5.42) may be expressed as

$$y^C_{i+1} = y_i + \frac{h}{2}(k_1 + k_2) \tag{5.43}$$

where

$$\left. \begin{array}{l} k_1 = f(x_i, y_i) \\ k_2 = f(x_i + h, y_i + hk_1) \end{array} \right\} \tag{5.44}$$

The method then has the form of a *Runge-Kutta* method of order 2.

A Runge–Kutta method of order r is any method of the form

$$y_{i+1}^C = y_i + h \sum_{p=1}^{r} w_p k_p \bigg/ \sum_{p=1}^{r} w_p \tag{5.45}$$

for

$$k_p = f(x_i + \alpha_p h, y_i + h \sum_{q=1}^{p-1} \beta_{pq} k_q) \quad (p = 1, \ldots, r)$$

where $w_p, \alpha_p, \beta_{pq}$ are so chosen that the expansion in powers of h of (5.45) agrees with that of y_{i+1} up to terms in h^r. In particular the Euler–trapezium method corresponds to $r = 2$ with

$$w_1 = w_2 = \tfrac{1}{2}, \quad \alpha_1 = 0, \quad \alpha_2 = 1, \quad \beta_{21} = 1$$

Can we find higher order Runge–Kutta methods? Yes we can, and we do this by determining systems of equations which must be satisfied by the parameters $w_p, \alpha_p, \beta_{pq}$. Details of such an analysis are too complicated for us to discuss here, and the reader is referred to Reference 1 for full information. However, we shall give formulae for popular third and fourth order Runge–Kutta methods and will verify that the third order formula indeed matches y_{i+1} to terms in h^3.

5.4.1 Third order Runge–Kutta

A popular third order method, which is closely related to Simpson's rule (see Reference 2), is given by

$$y_{i+1}^C = y_i + \frac{h}{6}(k_1 + 4k_2 + k_3) \tag{5.46}$$

where

$$\left. \begin{array}{l} k_1 = f(x_i, y_i) \\ k_2 = f(x_i + \tfrac{1}{2}h, y_i + \tfrac{1}{2}hk_1) \\ k_3 = f(x_i + h, y_i + h(2k_2 - k_1)) \end{array} \right\} \tag{5.47}$$

(Here $w_1 = w_3 = \tfrac{1}{3}$, $w_2 = \tfrac{4}{3}$; $\alpha_1 = 0$, $\alpha_2 = \tfrac{1}{2}$, $\alpha_3 = 1$; $\beta_{21} = \tfrac{1}{2}$, $\beta_{32} = 2$, $\beta_{31} = -1$.)

Now, from (3.4) above, dropping the subscript i from all terms $f, f_x,$ etc.,

$$y_{i+1} = y_i + hf + \tfrac{1}{2}h^2(f_x + ff_y)$$
$$+ \tfrac{1}{6}h^3(f_{xx} + 2ff_{xy} + f^2 f_{yy} + f_x f_y + ff_y^2) + O(h^4) \tag{5.48}$$

Let us therefore check that y_{i+1}^C, given by (5.46), has an expansion of the same form as (5.48). Now k_1, k_2, k_3 need only be expanded to terms in h^2. Thus

$$k_1 = f$$

$$k_2 = f + (\tfrac{1}{2}hf_x + \tfrac{1}{2}hk_1 f_y) + \frac{1}{2!}\tfrac{1}{4}h^2(f_{xx} + 2k_1 f_{xy} + k_1^2 f_{yy}) + \dots$$

$$= f + \tfrac{1}{2}h(f_x + ff_y) + \tfrac{1}{8}h^2(f_{xx} + 2ff_{xy} + f^2 f_{yy}) + O(h^3)$$

$$k_3 = f + h[f_x + (2k_2 - k_1)f_y]$$
$$\quad + \tfrac{1}{2}h^2[f_{xx} + 2(2k_2 - k_1)f_{xy} + (2k_2 - k_1)^2 f_{yy}] + O(h^3)$$

$$= f + h\{f_x + [f + h(f_x + ff_y)]f_y\}$$
$$\quad + \tfrac{1}{2}h^2(f_{xx} + 2ff_{xy} + f^2 f_{yy}) + O(h^3)$$

$$= f + h(f_x + ff_y) + \frac{h^2}{2}[2f_y(f_x + ff_y) + f_{xx} + 2ff_{xy} + f^2 f_{yy}] + O(h^3)$$

Hence

$$\tfrac{1}{6}(k_1 + 4k_2 + k_3)$$

$$= f + \frac{h}{2}(f_x + ff_y) + \frac{h^2}{6}(f_{xx} + 2ff_{xy} + f^2 f_{yy} + f_x f_y + ff_y^2) + O(h^3)$$

It immediately follows that (5.46) agrees with (5.48) to terms in h^3, and so (5.46), (5.47) is a third order Runge–Kutta method.

We shall not give a program for this method, since there is a surprisingly simple fourth order method which is rather more popular (and of course more accurate).

5.4.2 Fourth order Runge–Kutta

The classical fourth order Runge–Kutta formula is

$$y_{i+1}^C = y_i + \frac{h}{6}(k_1 + 2k_2 + 2k_3 + k_4) \qquad (5.49)$$

where

$$k_1 = f(x_i, y_i), \quad k_2 = f(x_i + \tfrac{1}{2}h, y_i + \tfrac{1}{2}hk_1)$$
$$k_3 = f(x_i + \tfrac{1}{2}h, y_i + \tfrac{1}{2}hk_2), \quad k_4 = f(x_{i+1}, y_i + hk_3) \qquad (5.50)$$

We shall not verify that y_{i+1}^C and y_i differ only in terms of $O(h^5)$, since the details are much more extensive even than those of Section 5.4.1, but the reader is referred to Reference 1 for the facts. The algorithm and corresponding program follow.

Algorithm 5.5 Fourth order Runge–Kutta for first order equation $y' = f(x, y)$

Define x_0, step h, number of steps n, initial value y_0, and function $f(x, y)$.
Calculate $y_1, \ldots, y_n$ from (5.49), (5.50) (for $i = 0, 1, \ldots, n-1$).

Program 5.5 RKFOUR: Fourth order classical Runge–Kutta method

```
    LIST
10REM- RKFOUR: 4TH ORDER CLASSICAL
20REM- RUNGE-KUTTA METHOD FOR EQN
30REM- Y'=F(X,Y), Y(X0)=Y0.
40 DEF FNF(X,Y)=X-.1*Y*Y
50PRINT "NO OF STEPS, X STEP";
60INPUT N,H
70PRINT "1ST X, 1ST Y";
80INPUT X0,Y0
90 PRINT "X:"," ";"Y:"
100FOR I=0 TO N-1
110K1=H*FNF(X0,Y0)
120K2=H*FNF(X0+.5*H,Y0+.5*K1)
130K3=H*FNF(X0+.5*H,Y0+.5*K2)
140K4=H*FNF(X0+H,Y0+K3)
150X0=X0+H
160Y0=Y0+(K1+2*K2+2*K3+K4)/6
170PRINT X0;" ";Y0
180NEXT I
190END
>
```

Sample run 1

```
RUN
NO OF STEPS, X STEP?10,.1
1ST X, 1ST Y?0,1
X:       Y:
    0.1 0.995066027
    0.2 1.00013042
    0.3 1.01499469
    0.4 1.03945848
    0.5 1.07331434
    0.6 1.11634281
    0.7 1.16830825
    0.8 1.22895586
    0.9 1.29800465
      1 1.37515293
>
```

Sample run 2

```
40      DEF FNF(X, Y)=X+Y
>RUN
NO OF STEPS, X STEP?10,.1
1ST X, 1ST Y?0,1
X:       Y:
    0.1 1.11034167
    0.2 1.24280514
    0.3 1.39971699
    0.4 1.58364848
    0.5 1.79744128
    0.6 2.04423593
    0.7 2.32750325
    0.8 2.65107913
    0.9 3.01920203
      1 3.43655949
>
```

Program notes

(1) The variables X0,Y0 are used for all x, y values.
(2) The program is set up and tested in Sample run 1 for the problem

$$y' = x - 0.1y^2, \quad y(0) = 1$$

The true $y(1)$ is 1.3751530, which is very accurately determined.
(3) In Sample run 2, $y' = x + y$ is solved. The true value of $y(1) = 3.436564$ is obtained correct to five decimal places.

5.5 Predictor–corrector methods of Adams type

In the last section the Euler–trapezium method was viewed as a second order Runge–Kutta method, and it became clear that there were more accurate methods in this class of methods, in particular the classical fourth order method of Algorithm 5.5. Let us now return to our original view of the Euler–trapezium method as a predictor–corrector method and see if we can obtain methods of this general type which have higher order accuracy.

The Euler–trapezium method was derived in Section 5.2 by approximately integrating $f(x, y(x))$ with respect to x, using the relation

$$y_{i+1} - y_i = \int_{x_i}^{x_{i+1}} f(x, y(x)) \, dx \tag{5.51}$$

The Adams–Bashforth and Adams–Moulton formulae, which provide higher order predictors and correctors, are obtained by replacing $f(x, y(x))$ by an interpolation polynomial (based on forward or backward finite differences) and then integrating from x_i to x_{i+1}.

Denoting $f(x_i, y_i)$ by f_i, we interpolate a polynomial $f = P_m(x)$ of degree m ($\leqslant i$) through the $m + 1$ points

$$(x_i, f_i), (x_{i-1}, f_{i-1}), \ldots, (x_{i-m}, f_{i-m})$$

Using the Newton backward difference interpolation formula (Reference 2, page 116) we obtain

$$P_m(x) = f_i + \binom{p}{1}\nabla f_i + \binom{p+1}{2}\nabla^2 f_i + \binom{p+2}{3}\nabla^3 f_i + \ldots$$
$$+ \binom{p+m-1}{m}\nabla^m f_i \tag{5.52}$$

where

$$x = x_i + ph \tag{5.53}$$

and

$$\binom{p+j-1}{j} \equiv \frac{(p+j-1)(p+j-2)\ldots(p)}{1 \times 2 \times \ldots j} \quad \text{(for } j = 1, 2, \ldots, m)$$

Thus

$$P_m(x) = \sum_{j=0}^{m} \binom{p+j-1}{j}\nabla^j f_i \tag{5.54}$$

Replacing $f(x, y(x))$ by $P_m(x)$ in (5.51) and using (5.53), we obtain the formula

$$y_{i+1}^C - y_i = \int_{x_i}^{x_{i+1}} P_m(x) \, dx = \int_0^1 \sum_{j=0}^{m} \binom{p+j-1}{j}\nabla^j f_i h \, dp$$

Defining

$$b_j = \int_0^1 \binom{p+j-1}{j} dp \tag{5.55}$$

we deduce that

$$y_{i+1}^C = y_i + h(b_0 f_i + b_1 \nabla f_i + \ldots + b_m \nabla^m f_i) \tag{5.56}$$

The coefficients b_j are easily calculated once and for all, by integration in (5.55), as

$$b_0 = 1, \quad b_1 = \tfrac{1}{2}, \quad b_2 = \tfrac{5}{12}, \quad b_3 = \tfrac{3}{8}, \quad b_4 = \tfrac{251}{720}, \quad \text{etc.} \tag{5.57}$$

The pair of formulae (5.56), (5.57) is called the Adams–Bashforth method.

Let us first give a concrete example of (5.56). If we set $m = 3$, then

$$\begin{aligned}
y_{i+1} &= y_i + h(f_i + \tfrac{1}{2}\nabla f_i + \tfrac{5}{12}\nabla^2 f_i + \tfrac{3}{8}\nabla^3 f_i) \\
&= y_i + h[f_i + \tfrac{1}{2}(f_i - f_{i+1}) + \tfrac{5}{12}(f_i - 2f_{i-1} + f_{i-2}) \\
&\quad + \tfrac{3}{8}(f_i - 3f_{i-1} + 3f_{i-2} - f_{i-3})]
\end{aligned}$$

i.e.

$$y_{i+1} = y_i + \frac{h}{24}(55f_i - 59f_{i-1} + 37f_{i-2} - 9f_{i-3}) \quad (i = 3, 4, \ldots) \tag{5.58}$$

whereas for $m = 0$ we simply obtain Euler's method

$$y_{i+1} = y_i + hf_i$$

More generally, by replacing differences $\nabla f_i, \nabla^2 f_i, \ldots$ by combinations of $f_i, f_{i-1}, \ldots$, the general formula (5.56) may be written in the form

$$y_{i+1} = y_i + h(\beta_0 f_i + \beta_1 f_{i-1} + \ldots + \beta_m f_{i-m}) \tag{5.59}$$

where $\beta_0, \beta_1, \ldots, \beta_m$ are certain constants.

However, although (5.59) may seem more convenient, please note that $b_0, b_1, b_2, \ldots$ are *absolute constants* (independent of m) whereas $\beta_0, \beta_1, \beta_2, \ldots$ change for each m, and so (5.56) is the *basic formula*.

Clearly, if the formula (5.58) is to be used, it can only be applied for $i = 3, 4, \ldots$ to determine $y_4, y_5 \ldots$ Some *starting procedure* is therefore needed to determine y_1, y_2, y_3 from y_0. More generally, a starting procedure is needed for (5.56) which determines $y_1, y_2, \ldots, y_m$ from y_0. Before we can proceed in this area, however, we must determine the *order* of the formula (5.56) and more specifically (5.58), since this dictates the choice of the starting procedure.

5.5.1 Order and error of the Adams–Bashforth method

The error in the approximation $P_m(x)$ to $f(x, y(x))$ is approximately proportional to $\nabla^{m+1} f_i$ (see (5.52)) and we showed in Reference 2 that this was in turn proportional to h^{m+1}.

More specifically

$$\nabla^{m+1} f_i \simeq h^{m+1} f_i^{(m+1)} \tag{5.60}$$

where $f_i^{(m+1)}$ denotes the $(m+1)$th derivative of f at x_i. (For example, $\nabla f_i \simeq h f_i'$.) Hence

$$y_{i+1} - y_i \simeq \int_{x_i}^{x_{i+1}} [P_m(x) + b_{m+1} h^{m+1} f_i^{(m+1)}] \, dx$$

$$= \int_0^1 P_m(x) \, dx + b_{m+1} \int_0^1 h^{m+1} f_i^{(m+1)} h \, dp$$

$$= (y_{i+1}^C - y_i) + b_{m+1} h^{m+2} f_i^{(m+1)}$$

i.e.

$$y_{i+1} - y_{i+1}^C \simeq b_{m+1} h^{m+2} f_i^{(m+1)} = O(h^{m+2}) \tag{5.61}$$

Thus the Adams–Bashforth method (5.56) is of *order* $m+1$; and in particular (5.58) is a fourth order method, which should therefore be of comparable accuracy with the classical Runge–Kutta method (5.49).

The error in (5.60) is a local truncation error. Thus the global truncation error $T(y_n)$ at a general point $x = x_n$ will be

$$T(y_n) = n O(h^{m+2}) = O(h^{m+1}), \quad \text{since } n = (x - x_0)/h$$

Clearly then the global truncation error will reach $O(h^{m+1})$, assuming that the starting values are determined by a method of order $m+1$.

Thus the fourth order (classical) Runge–Kutta method provides an appropriately accurate method to use to calculate starting values for the fourth order Adams–Bashforth method.

The approximate local truncation error (5.61) can be determined precisely for any particular m, once $b_0, b_1, \ldots, b_{m+1}$ have been calculated. Thus the error in the fourth order Adams–Bashforth formula (5.58) is given by

$$y_{i+1} - y_{i+1}^{AB} \simeq b_4 h^5 f_i^{(4)} = \tfrac{251}{720} h^5 f_i^{(4)} \tag{5.62}$$

[The suffix AB is used in place of C to denote the value computed by the Adams–Bashforth method.]

5.5.2 Adams–Bashforth algorithm

The information above enables us to produce an algorithm and program for a fourth order Adams–Bashforth method. However, this is not yet a predictor–corrector method, it is simply an *explicit method* (i.e. one which yields y_{i+1} directly from $y_i, y_{i-1}, \ldots$).

As a starting procedure we need a fourth order explicit method based only on the value of y_i, and for this purpose the fourth order Runge–Kutta method (5.49) is a natural choice.

Algorithm 5.6 Fourth order Adams–Bashforth for $y' = f(x, y)$

Define x_0, h, n, y_0 and $f(x, y)$.
Calculate y_1, y_2, y_3 from (5.49) ($i = 0, 1, 2$).
Calculate $y_4, y_5, \ldots, y_n$ from (5.58) ($i = 3, 4, \ldots, n-1$).

Program 5.6   ADBASH: Fourth order Adams–Bashforth method

```
LIST
 10REM- ADBASH: ADAMS-BASHFORTH
 20REM- 4TH ORDER MULTI-STEP METHOD
 30REM- WITH 4TH ORDER RUNGE-KUTTA
 40REM- METHOD AS STARTER, FOR EQN
 50REM- Y'=F(X,Y), Y(X0)=Y0.
 60DEF FNF(X,Y)=X+Y
 70DIM F(100)
 80PRINT "NO OF STEPS, X STEP"
 90INPUT N,H
100PRINT "1ST X, 1ST Y";
110INPUT X0,Y0
120PRINT "X"," ";"Y","    ";"F(X,Y)"
130F(0)=FNF(X0,Y0)
140PRINT X0;" ";Y0;" ";F(0)
150REM- 4TH ORDER R-K METHOD GIVES
160REM- Y1,Y2,Y3 AND HENCE F1,F2,F3
170FOR I=1 TO 3
180K1=FNF(X0,Y0)
190K2=FNF(X0+.5*H,Y0+.5*H*K1)
200K3=FNF(X0+.5*H,Y0+.5*H*K2)
210K4=FNF(X0+H,Y0+H*K3)
220X0=X0+H
230Y0=Y0+H*(K1+2*K2+2*K3+K4)/6
240F(I)=FNF(X0,Y0)
250PRINT X0;" ";Y0;" ";F(I)
260NEXT I
270REM- ADAMS-BASHFORTH (M=3).
280FOR I=3 TO N-1
290X0=X0+H
300Y0=Y0+H*(55*F(I)-59*F(I-1)+37*F(I-2)-9*F(I-3))/24
310F(I+1)=FNF(X0,Y0)
320PRINT X0;" ";Y0;" ";F(I+1)
330NEXT I
340END
>
```

Sample run

```
RUN                              0.3 1.39971699 1.69971699
NO OF STEPS, X STEP              0.4 1.58364021 1.98364021
?10,.1                           0.5 1.79742198 2.29742198
1ST X, 1ST Y?0,1                 0.6 2.04420415 2.64420415
X        Y         F(X,Y)        0.7 2.3274565 3.0274565
       0 1 1                     0.8 2.65101448 3.45101448
       0.1 1.11034167 1.21034167 0.9 3.01911706 3.91911706
       0.2 1.24280514 1.44280514 1 3.43644888 4.43644888
                            >
```

Program notes

(1) The variables XO,YO are used for all x, y values, but the subscripted variable F(I) is used for $f_i = f(x_i, y_i)$.
(2) In the sample run, $y' = x + y$ is solved, and the results may be compared with those of Sample run 2 of Program 5.5. They are correct to four decimal places and so are slightly less accurate.

5.6 Adams–Moulton predictor–corrector method

In Section 5.2 we used the trapezium rule, which is implicit, as a corrector to improve on the solution obtained by Euler's method. Let us now therefore seek an implicit formula to use as a corrector to pair with the more accurate Adams–Bashforth method. Such a formula is obtained by replacing $f(x, y(x))$ in (5.51) by a polynomial $Q_m(x)$ of degree m which interpolates (x, f) in the $m + 1$ points

$$(x_{i+1}, f_{i+1}), (x_i, f_i), \ldots, (x_{i-m+1}, f_{i+m+1})$$

Using the Newton backward difference formula again, we obtain

$$Q_m(x) = f_{i+1} + \binom{p}{1} \nabla f_{i+1} + \binom{p+1}{2} \nabla^2 f_{i+1} + \ldots$$

$$+ \binom{p+m-1}{m} \nabla^m f_{i+1} = \sum_{j=0}^{m} \binom{p+j-1}{j} \nabla^j f_{i+1} \qquad (5.63)$$

where

$$x = x_{i+1} + ph \qquad (5.64)$$

Replacing $f(x, y(x))$ by $Q_m(x)$ in (5.51), we obtain

$$y_{i+1}^C - y_i = \int_{x_i}^{x_{i+1}} Q_m(x)\, dx = h \int_{-1}^{0} \sum_{j=0}^{m} \binom{p+j-1}{j} \nabla^j f_{i+1}\, dp$$

Hence

$$y_{i+1}^C = y_i + h(c_0 f_{i+1} + c_1 \nabla f_{i+1} + \ldots + c_m \nabla^m f_{i+1}) \quad (i \geqslant m-1) \quad (5.65)$$

where

$$c_j = \int_{-1}^{0} \binom{p+j-1}{j}\, dp \qquad (5.66)$$

The coefficients c_j are easily calculated once and for all from (5.66) as

$$c_0 = 1, \quad c_1 = -\tfrac{1}{2}, \quad c_2 = -\tfrac{1}{12}, \quad c_3 = -\tfrac{1}{24}, \quad c_4 = -\tfrac{19}{720}, \quad \text{etc.} \,(5.67)$$

The formula (5.65) is termed the Adams–Moulton corrector. As a concrete example, set $m = 3$. Then

$$
\begin{aligned}
y^C_{i+1} &= y_i + h(f_{i+1} - \tfrac{1}{2}\nabla f_{i+1} - \tfrac{1}{12}\nabla^2 f_{i+1} - \tfrac{1}{24}\nabla^3 f_{i+1}) \\
&= y_i + h[f_{i+1} - \tfrac{1}{2}(f_{i+1} - f_i) - \tfrac{1}{12}(f_{i+1} - 2f_i + f_{i-1}) \\
&\quad - \tfrac{1}{24}(f_{i+1} - 3f_i + 3f_{i-1} - f_{i-2})]
\end{aligned}
$$

Thus

$$
y^C_{i+1} = y_i + \frac{h}{24}(9f_{i+1} + 19f_i - 5f_{i-1} + f_{i-2}) \tag{5.68}
$$

By a similar argument to that of Section 5.5.1 above, we may deduce that (5.65) is an $(m + 1)$ th order method and in particular that (5.68) is a *fourth order method*. Similarly it follows for the fourth order method (5.68) that

$$
y_{i+1} - y^C_{i+1} \simeq c_{m+1} h^{m+2} f^{(m+1)}_{i+1} = -\tfrac{19}{720} h^5 f_{i+1} \tag{5.69}
$$

Now, by Taylor series,

$$
f^{(4)}_{i+1} = f^{(4)}(x_i + h) = f^{(4)}(x_i) + O(h) \tag{5.70}
$$

and on substitution in (5.69) this gives

$$
y_{i+1} - y^{AM}_{i+1} \simeq -\tfrac{19}{720} h^5 f^{(4)}_i \tag{5.71}
$$

[The suffix AM is used in place of C to denote the value computed by the Adams–Moulton corrector.]

Comparing this local truncation error with that (5.62) of the fourth order Adams–Bashforth method, we see that the constant $251/720$ has been replaced by $-19/720$, and hence the error is reduced by a factor of about 13. Thus the Adams–Moulton corrector is of the same order but significantly more accurate than the Adams–Bashforth method. This pair of formulae is therefore compatible as a predictor and corrector in a predictor–corrector method. However, there is an even greater advantage to this pairing. For, on combining (5.71) and (5.62),

$$
y_{i+1} - y^{AM}_{i+1} \simeq -\tfrac{19}{270}(y^{AM}_{i+1} - y^{AB}_{i+1}) \tag{5.72}
$$

This formula (5.72) gives us an estimate of the error in the final value obtained from the Adams–Moulton corrector, based on the difference between predicted and corrected values.

This possibility for estimating the error gives the Adams–Moulton (AM) fourth order predictor–corrector method, which we formally define below, a strong advantage over the classical (fourth order) Runge–Kutta method. This advantage has to be balanced, of course, against the greater simplicity of the Runge–Kutta method and in particular the complication of having to use a Runge–Kutta (RK) (or other explicit method of fourth order) to start off the Adams–Moulton method. It should also be added that the AM method has better stability properties than the RK method (see Section 5.7 below).

Strictly speaking, the analysis which leads to error estimate (5.72) and the local truncation error estimate (5.71) is based on the implicit rule (5.68), in which the same value of y_{i+1}^{AM} is used on both left- and right-hand sides. In practice the value y_{i+1}^{AB}, obtained from the predictor, is actually used on the right, and therefore the formula (5.65) only holds when repeated Adams–Moulton corrections have been applied. However, in general the error estimate (5.72) is quite realistic even when only one correction is used.

Algorithm 5.7 Adams–Moulton fourth order predictor–corrector method

Define x_0, h, n, y_0, $f(x, y)$, and the number of correctors per step.
Calculate y_1, y_2, y_3 from (5.49) ($i = 0, 1, 2$).
For $i = 3, 4, \ldots, n - 1$:

Calculate y_{i+1}^{AB} from (5.58).

For $j = 1$ to p:

Calculate y_{i+1}^{AM} from (5.68) (using the latest value of y_{i+1} on the right-hand side).
Print out the estimated local truncation error (5.72) in y_{i+1}.

Program 5.7   ADMOULT: Adams–Moulton fourth order predictor–corrector method.

```
LIST
  10REM- ADMOULT: ADAMS-MOULTON 4TH
  20REM- ORDER PREDICTOR-CORRECTOR
  30REM- METHOD (BASED ON ADAMS-
  40REM- BASHFORTH PREDICTOR AND
  50REM- ADAMS-MOULTON CORRECTOR)
  60REM- WITH 4TH ORDER R-K STARTER
  70REM- FOR  Y'=F(X,Y), Y(X0)=Y0.
  80DEF FNF(X,Y)=X+Y
  90DIM F(100)
 100PRINT "NO OF STEPS, X STEP"
 110INPUT N,H
 120PRINT "1ST X,1ST Y";
 130INPUT X0,Y0
 140PRINT "X","    ";"Y","    ";" ERR"
 150F(0)=FNF(X0,Y0)
 160PRINT X0;"    ";Y0
 170REM- 4TH ORDER R-K METHOD GIVES
 180REM- Y1,Y2,Y3 AND HENCE F1,F2,F3
 190FOR I=1 TO 3
 200K1=FNF(X0,Y0)
```

```
210K2=FNF(X0+.5*H,Y0+.5*H*K1)
220K3=FNF(X0+.5*H,Y0+.5*H*K2)
230K4=FNF(X0+H,Y0+H*K3)
240X0=X0+H
250Y0=Y0+H*(K1+2*K2+2*K3+K4)/6
260F(I)=FNF(X0,Y0)
270PRINT X0;"    ";Y0
280NEXT I
290REM- ADAMS-MOULTON (M=3)
300FOR I=3 TO N-1
310X0=X0+H
320YAB=Y0+H*(55*F(I)-59*F(I-1)+37*F(I-2)-9*F(I-3))/24
330FAB=FNF(X0,YAB)
340PRINT X0;" P ";YAB
350Y0=Y0+H*(9*FAB+19*F(I)-5*F(I-1)+F(I-2))/24
360F(I+1)=FNF(X0,Y0)
370ERREST=19*(YAB-Y0)/251
380PRINT X0;" C ";Y0;" ";ERREST
390NEXT I
400END
```

Sample run

```
RUN
NO OF STEPS, X STEP
?10,.1
1ST X,1ST Y?0,1
X              Y                    ERR
        0      1
       0.1     1.11034167
       0.2     1.24280514
       0.3     1.39971699
       0.4  P. 1.58364021
       0.4  C  1.58364908   -6.23884369E-7
       0.5  P  1.79743288
       0.5  C  1.79744262   -6.85096408E-7
       0.6  P  2.04422733
       0.6  C  2.04423815   -7.61349306E-7
       0.7  P  2.32749459
       0.7  C  2.32750653   -8.40125399E-7
       0.8  P  2.65107046
       0.8  C  2.65108366   -9.28469968E-7
       0.9  P  3.01919425
       0.9  C  3.01920884   -1.02612086E-6
        1   P  3.43655112
        1   C  3.43656724   -1.13399561E-6
```

Program notes

(1) Variables X0,Y0,F(I) are used for x_i, y_i, f_i.

(2) In the sample run, $y' = x + y$ is again solved. The Adams–Moulton value YAM of y_i is noticeably more accurate than the Adams–Bashforth value YAB but closely comparable with the fourth order Runge–Kutta solution of Program 5.5. (The true $y(1)$ is 3.436537.)

5.6.1 Variable step–variable order methods

The Adams–Moulton predictor–corrector method is an extremely powerful method for solving ordinary differential equations, especially when the step h and the order $m + 1$ of the predictor and corrector are varied during the computation. Such adjustments, which are typically based on the error estimate (5.72), lead to great efficiency and versatility. It is beyond the scope of this book to say more, and the reader is referred to Reference 3 for details.

5.7 Rounding errors and stability

So far in this chapter our discussion of error has been restricted to truncation errors. However, rounding errors are of crucial importance in solving initial-value problems, and indeed some numerical methods can be highly unstable. Fortunately, and this is one reason why we have emphasized them, the Adams–Moulton (and Euler–trapezium) methods are stable for any h, and the classical Runge–Kutta method is stable for h suitably small.

5.7.1 Instability of the mid-point rule

Consider a new explicit method for solving

$$y' = f(x, y), \quad y(x_0) = y_0 = C$$

based on the approximation

$$y_{i+1} - y_{i-1} = 2hf(x_i, y_i), \quad y_0 = C \tag{5.73}$$

This is termed the *mid-point rule*, and it adopts a mean central difference approximation to y' at the point x_i. Now let us restrict attention to the particular equation

$$y' = Ay, \quad y(0) = 1 \tag{5.74}$$

which has the true solution $y = e^{Ax}$. In this case

$$f(x_i, y_i) = f_i = Ay_i$$

and hence (5.73) gives

$$y_{i+1} - 2Ahy_i - y_{i-1} = 0, \quad y_0 = 1 \tag{5.75}$$

This is a three-term recurrence relation and has the general solution

$$y_i = C_1(t_1)^i + C_2(t_2)^i \tag{5.76}$$

where t_1, t_2 are the roots of the quadratic equation

$$t^2 - 2Aht - 1 = 0 \tag{5.77}$$

and where C_1 and C_2 are some constants.

Let us restrict attention to the case $A = -1$, for simplicity. From (5.77),

$$t_1, t_2 = -h \pm \sqrt{(1+h^2)}$$
$$= -h \pm [1 + \tfrac{1}{2}h^2 + O(h^4)]$$

Thus

$$t_1 = 1 - h + \tfrac{1}{2}h^2 + O(h^4)$$
$$t_2 = -1 - h - \tfrac{1}{2}h^2 + O(h^4)$$

Now

$$e^h = 1 + h + \tfrac{1}{2}h^2 + O(h^3)$$

and hence

$$t_1 = e^{-h} + O(h^3), \quad t_2 = -e^h + O(h^3)$$

Thus

$$y_i = C_1[e^{-h} + O(h^3)]^i + C_2[-e^h + O(h^3)]^i$$

Now let

$$x = x_n = nh$$

Then

$$y_n = C_1[e^{-nh} + nO(h^3)] + C_2[e^{nh} + nO(h^3)](-1)^n$$
$$= C_1 e^{-x} + C_2(-1)^n e^x + O(h^2) \tag{5.78}$$

The true solution is e^{-x}, and thus we expect C_1, C_2 to have values $1, 0$. However, only one initial condition $y_0 = 1$ is available, and in practice C_1 and C_2 are only approximately $1, 0$. This means that the numerical solution (5.78) always has some contribution from the term $C_2(-1)^n e^x$. This is an exponentially growing function, and, however small C_2 is, the spurious term eventually dominates the numerical solution. The mid-point rule is therefore unstable for the equation (5.74) for $A = -1$ (and in fact for all negative A).

A numerical example of this instability is illustrated in *Table 5.1* for the case $A = -2.5$, where results are rounded at each step to two decimal places. Here we set $h = 0.1$ and $y_0 = 1, y_1 = 0.78$ (the latter being the correct value to two decimal places of $e^{-2.5x}$ at $x = 0.1$) and evaluated $y_2, y_3, \ldots$ from (5.75), namely

$$y_{i+1} = y_{i-1} - 0.5 y_i$$

Table 5.1. Mid-point rule for $y' = -2.5y$, $y(0) = 1$

x_i	y_i	x_i	y_i
0.1	0.78	1.1	0.10
0.2	0.61	1.2	0.01
0.3	0.48	1.3	0.10
0.4	0.37	1.4	-0.04
0.5	0.30	1.5	0.12
0.6	0.22	1.6	-0.10
0.7	0.19	1.7	0.17
0.8	0.12	1.8	-0.19
0.9	0.13	1.9	0.27
1.0	0.06	2.0	-0.32

5.7.2 Stability of the Adams–Moulton corrector

Consider the fourth order corrector (5.68) applied to the model equation (5.74); then, replacing f_i by Ay_i,

$$y_{i+1} = y_i + \frac{Ah}{24}(9y_{i+1} + 19y_i - 5y_{i+1} + y_{i-2})$$

Thus

$$(1 - 9\gamma)y_{i+1} - (1 + 19\gamma)y_i + 5\gamma y_{i-1} - \gamma y_{i-2} = 0 \qquad (5.79)$$

where

$$\gamma = Ah/24 = O(h) \qquad (5.80)$$

The general solution of (5.79) is of the form

$$y_i = C_1(t_1)^i + C_2(t_2)^i + C_3(t_3)^i \qquad (5.81)$$

where t_1, t_2, t_3 are the roots of the cubic equation

$$(1 - 9\gamma)t^3 - (1 + 19\gamma)t^2 + 5\gamma t - \gamma = 0$$

From (5.80), this equation becomes

$$t^3 - t^2 + O(h) = 0 \qquad (5.82)$$

Ignoring the term $O(h)$, it follows that the roots of (5.82) are approximately

$$t_1 = 1, \quad t_2 = 0, \quad t_3 = 0$$

The dominant term in y_i, from (5.81), is thus

$$y_i \simeq C_1(t_1)^i \qquad (5.83)$$

A more careful analysis (see Reference 1) shows that

$$t_1 = 1 + Ah + O(h^2) = e^{Ah} + O(h^2)$$
$$t_2, t_3 \simeq \pm(-Ah/24)^{\frac{1}{3}}$$

Thus, at $x = x_n = nh$, (5.81) gives

$$y_n \simeq C_1 e^{Ax} + [C_2 + (-1)^n C_3](-Ah/24)^{n/2} \tag{5.84}$$

Here $C_1 \simeq 1$, since e^{Ax} is the true solution, and $C_2 \simeq C_3 \simeq 0$.
Clearly small errors in C_1, C_2 and C_3 have little relative effect on the computed solution, since the second term in (5.84) is small, and so the Adams–Moulton corrector is stable for the model equation (5.74) for all A.

5.8 Second and higher order differential equations

In Section 5.3 we extended the Euler–trapezium predictor–corrector method from first to second order differential equations. This was achieved by introducing a new dependent variable $z = y'$, reducing the second order equation to a pair of first order equations in y and z, expressing the new problem as a single-vector first order equation in $\mathbf{y} = (y \quad z)^{\mathrm{T}}$, and adopting the Euler–trapezium rule in a vector form. Precisely the same technique can be used to extend the Runge–Kutta and Adams–Moulton methods to second order equations, and we leave the programming of this as an exercise to the reader.

More generally we may extend all the methods of this chapter to initial-value problems of any order. For example, the problem

$$y''' = g(x, y, y', y''), \quad y(0) = C, \quad y'(0) = D, \quad y''(0) = E$$

reduces to the system

$$\mathbf{y}' = f(x, \mathbf{y}), \quad \mathbf{y}(x_0) = \mathbf{C}$$

where

$$\mathbf{y} = (y \quad z_1 \quad z_2)^{\mathrm{T}}, \quad \mathbf{f}(x, \mathbf{y}) = (z_1 \quad z_2 \quad g(x, y, z_1, z_2))^{\mathrm{T}}$$
$$\mathbf{C} = (C \quad D \quad E)^{\mathrm{T}}, \quad z_1 = y', z_2 = y''$$

5.9 References

1. PHILLIPS, G.M. and TAYLOR, P.J., *Theory and Applications of Numerical Analysis*, Academic Press, London (1973)
2. MASON, J.C., *BASIC Numerical Mathematics*, Butterworths (1983)
3. HALL, G. and WATT, J.M., (Eds.), *Modern Numerical Methods for Ordinary Differential Equations*, Clarendon Press (1976)

PROBLEMS

(5.1) Calculate approximate values of $y(0), y(0.1), y(0.2), \ldots, y(1.0)$ by Euler's method from the differential equation

$$y' = 4y, \quad y(0) = 1$$

for the choices (i) $h = 0.1$, (ii) $h = 0.05$, (iii) $h = 0.025$. To what values are the numerical solutions converging?

(5.2) Use Program 5.2 to solve correct to three decimal places for $0 \leqslant x \leqslant 1$ the following problems with appropriate choices of h:
   (i) $y' = 1 + y^2$, $y(0) = 0$
   (ii) $y' = 1 + 2xy$, $y(0) = 0$
   (iii) $y' = x + y$, $y(0) = 0$
What are the known solutions at $x = 1$ for (i) and (iii), and how do they compare with the computed solutions?

(5.3) The equation of motion of a truck, which strikes a viscously damped buffer, may be written as

$$m \frac{dv}{dt} = -cv, \quad \text{with } v(0) = v_0 \text{ given}$$

Use Programs 5.1, 5.3 to find the velocity of the truck at time $t = 0.8$ s, given that it has mass $m = 4000$ kg, the damping coefficient is $c = 10000 \text{ N s m}^{-1}$ and the initial velocity is 2 m s^{-1}. Test Euler's method with (i) 10 steps and then (ii) 100 steps, and test the Euler–trapezium method with 10 steps and (i) 1, (ii) 2, (iii) 4 corrections per step.

(5.4) The angular velocity ω of a turbine, initially ω_0, decreases according to the equation

$$J\dot{\omega} + C\omega + M = 0$$

where J = moment of inertia, C = viscous torque coefficient, and M = dry friction torque.
   Use the fourth order Runge–Kutta method to determine how long the turbine takes to come to rest from an initial velocity of 5000 radians per minute, given that the turbine has mass 500 kg and radius of gyration 0.12 m, and that $C = 0.12$ N m s, $M = 8$ N m. [Check: $\omega = 0$ at $t = 48.7$ s. What is the solution in closed form?]

(5.5) Consider $y' = x + y$, $y(0) = 0$.
   Determine, by trial and error, a choice of step h which is (just) sufficient to ensure that $y(1)$ is computed correct to four decimal places using (i) Euler's method, (ii) fourth order Runge–Kutta and (iii) Adams–Moulton.

Compare the total numbers of evaluations of $f(x, y)$ that are used in each method, and hence determine which method is the most efficient.

(5.6) A vertical spring–dashpot system satisfies the equation of motion $m\ddot{x} = mg - c\dot{x} - kx$ where m is the mass, g is the gravitational acceleration, c is the dashpot constant, and k is the modulus (per unit length) of the spring. Initially the displacement x and velocity $\dot{x}$ of the system are zero.

Use the Euler–trapezium method to determine the maximum displacement and the time at which it occurs, given that $m = 1000\,\text{kg}$, $k = 10\,000\,\text{N m}^{-1}$, and $c = 4000\,\text{N s m}^{-1}$. [Maximum is 1.056 at $t = 1.283\,\text{s}$.]

(5.7) The angular movement (θ) of a car fuel gauge needle is given by the second order equation

$$\ddot{\theta} + 2G\omega\dot{\theta} + \omega^2\theta = \omega^2\theta_{ss}$$

subject to

$$\dot{\theta} = \theta = 0 \quad \text{at } t = 0$$

where θ_{ss} is the steady state angular movement, G is the non-dimensional damping ratio, and ω is the undamped natural frequency.

Tabulate the angular movement θ/θ_{ss} at intervals of 0.1 s up to the time 2 s, given that $G = 2.0$ and $\omega = 11\,\text{rads s}^{-1}$. Use a step length of 0.01 s and the Euler–trapezium method (Program 5.4). Repeat your solution for $G = 0.8$. [At time $t = 0.5\,\text{s}$, $\theta/\theta_{ss} = 0.753$ when $G = 2.0$.]

(5.8) The equation of a cantilever beam has the form

$$EI(x)y'' = M(x), \quad y(0) = y'(0) = 0$$

where y is the displacement at the point x of a beam of length l, E is the Young's modulus, $I(x)$ is the second moment of area, and $M(x)$ is the bending moment.

Determine the bending moment $M(x)$ in terms of x, and hence calculate by the Euler–trapezium method the displacement $y(x)$ at steps of $h = 0.025$ when $l = 1$ for the following two types of beam:
  (i) an end-loaded unit length cantilever with $EI = W = 1$ ($W = $ load)
  (ii) the tapered cantilever support shown in *Figure 5.2*
[Check:

$$\frac{M(x)}{EI} = l - x, \quad \frac{q}{EI_0} = \left(\frac{2l^3 - 3l^2x + x^3}{6(3l - 2x)}\right) \text{ in (i), (ii)}]$$

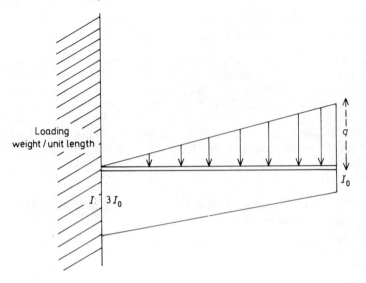

Figure 5.2. Tapered cantilever.

(5.9) Write a program to carry out the third order Runge–Kutta method (5.46), (5.47) and use it to solve problems (5.2)(i), (ii). Compare this program's performance with that of the fourth order Runge–Kutta method (Program 5.5) for these problems.

(5.10) Verify that the classical Runge–Kutta formula (5.49) has a local truncation error of $O(h^5)$. [Use a similar technique to that of Section 5.4.1 for third order Runge–Kutta.]

(5.11) Prove that the Adams–Bashforth method is stable for the model equation $y' = Ay$ for all A. [Hint: Use similar calculations to those of Section 5.7.2.]

(5.12) Use the Adams–Moulton fourth order predictor–corrector method to solve the problems (5.2)(i), (ii). How realistic are the local error estimates compared with the known errors?

(5.13) The second order Adams–Bashforth method for the solution of

$$y' = f(x, y), \quad y(x_0) = y_0$$

involves the approximate formula

$$y_{i+1} = y_i + hf_i + \tfrac{1}{2}h(f_i - f_{i-1})$$

(i) Verify that the local truncation error is $O(h^3)$.

(ii) Show that, for $f(x, y) = Ay$, the computed solution is

$$y_i = C_1(t_1)^i + C_2(t_2)^i$$
$$= C_1(t_1)^i[1 + C'(t_2/t_1)^i]$$

where t_1, t_2 are the roots of

$$t^2 - t(1 - 3Ah/2) - Ah/2 = 0$$

(iii) If $h < 2/(3A)$, so that $1 - 3Ah/2 > 0$, show that

$$|t_2/t_1| < 1$$

and deduce that, for such small values of h, the method is stable. [Note: The method is unconditionally stable by other arguments.]

(5.14) Write a program which uses the fourth order Runge–Kutta method for the solution of

$$y'' = g(x, y, y'), \quad y(0) = C, \quad y'(0) = D$$

based on reduction of the problem to a pair of first order equations (see the development of Program 5.4). Test this program on one of the problems (5.4)–(5.6) above.

(5.15) Write a program which uses the Adams–Moulton method for the solution of

$$y'' = y(x, y, y'), \quad y(0) = C, \quad y'(0) = D$$

based on a reduction of the problem to a pair of first order equations, and test the program on one of the problems (5.6)–(5.8) above.

(5.16) Write a program which uses the Euler–trapezium rule for the solution of

$$y''' = g(x, y, y', y''), \quad y(0) = C, \quad y'(0) = D, \quad y''(0) = E$$

based on the reduction of the problem to three first order equations and modelled on Program 5.4.

Hence solve for $y(x)$, from $x = 0$ to $x = 4$ in steps of 0.1, the *Blasius equation*

$$y''' = -yy'', \quad y(0) = 0, \quad y'(0) = 0, \quad y''(0) = 1$$

Chapter 6

Boundary-value problems

ESSENTIAL THEORY

6.1 Introduction

In the previous chapter we considered initial-value problems, in which all the boundary conditions of the problem were specified at the same x value. The numerical methods that we used to solve these problems involved the calculation of one y value at a time, y_{i+1}, in terms of previous values $y_i, y_{i-1}, \ldots, y_0$, by formulae which effectively involved explicit calculations. Indeed even corrector formulae, which are often referred to as implicit, typically need only be applied a few times before sufficiently accurate results are obtained.

However, boundary-value problems contrast significantly with initial-value problems in a number of areas. In two respects they are more difficult to solve and in two respects less so. Firstly, the boundary conditions in such problems are prescribed at distinct points. For example, a beam of length l supported simply at each end (see *Figure 6.1*) satisfies the differential equation

$$EIy'' = M(x) \tag{6.1}$$

subject to the boundary conditions

$$y(0) = y(l) = 0 \tag{6.2}$$

where $y(x)$ and $M(x)$ respectively denote the unknown deflection and known bending moment at distance x from one end, and E, I denote the Young's modulus and second moment of area. Secondly, since we do not know the gradient $y'(x)$ at either end we cannot adopt a method to determine one y value at a time as in Chapter 5, but rather

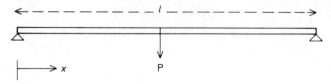

Figure 6.1. Simply supported, centrally loaded beam.

104

we must solve for y values at all stations simultaneously. Thirdly, and now we move on to potential advantages, boundary-value problems are generally better conditioned than initial-value problems, essentially because the solution is 'tied down' at more than one point. Fourthly, for related reasons, instability is not normally a significant difficulty in boundary-value problems. Before considering a specific numerical solution, we introduce in the next two sections two key steps in the calculation.

6.2 Finite-difference approximations to derivatives

In Chapter 3, we derived and discussed finite-difference approximations to y_i', y_i'' (namely y', y'' at $x = x_i$), and noted that consistent local errors of $O(h^2)$ were obtained by using the *central difference* formulae

$$y_i' = \frac{1}{2h}(y_{i+1} - y_{i-1}) \tag{6.3}$$

$$y_i'' = \frac{1}{h^2}(y_{i+1} - 2y_i + y_{i-1}) \tag{6.4}$$

These formulae combine accuracy and simplicity, and we shall use them wherever possible in boundary-value problems.

Consider first of all the second order differential equation (for y)

$$p(x)y'' + q(x)y' + r(x)y = s(x) \tag{6.5}$$

where p, q, r, s are given functions of x. Then, at the station $x = x_i$ ($= x_0 + ih$), this gives

$$p_i y_i'' + q_i y_i' + r_i y_i = x_i \tag{6.6}$$

where p_i, q_i, r_i, s_i denote $p(x_i), q(x_i), r(x_i), s(x_i)$.

If we substitute (6.3), (6.4) into (6.6) then we obtain (for each station i) a linear equation in y_{i+1}, y_i and y_{i-1}. Specifically

$$\frac{p_i}{h^2}(y_{i+1} - 2y_i + y_{i-1}) + \frac{q_i}{2h}(y_{i+1} - y_{i-1}) + r_i y_i = s_i$$

Collecting corresponding y terms,

$$y_{i-1}\left(\frac{p_i}{h^2} + \frac{q_i}{2h}\right) + y_i\left(-\frac{2p_i}{h^2} + r_i\right) + y_{i+1}\left(\frac{p_i}{h^2} + \frac{q_i}{2h}\right) = s_i \tag{6.7}$$

Thus at each station we may easily set down a discrete linear equation (which does not involve derivatives) in place of the differential equation.

As far as boundary conditions are concerned, the same central differences may normally also be used. For example, if $x_0 = 0$ and $x_N = l$ are the first and last stations (with $h = l/N$), then elementary boundary conditions such as

$$y(0) = C, \quad y(l) = D \quad (C, D \text{ given}) \tag{6.8}$$

are immediately translated into

$$y_0 = C, \quad y_N = D \tag{6.9}$$

In this case the model (6.7) for the differential equation would only be applied at all interior stations $x_1, \ldots, x_{N-1}$. Equations (6.7) ($i = 1, \ldots, N-1$) and (6.9) comprise $N+1$ linear simultaneous equations for the unknowns $y_0, \ldots, y_N$. More simply, we may substitute for y_0, y_N from (6.9) into (6.7) to give $N-1$ equations for $y_1, \ldots, y_{N-1}$.

However, for less trivial boundary conditions such as

$$y'(0) = C, \quad y(l) = D \quad (C, D \text{ given}) \tag{6.10}$$

we would write (using (6.3) for $i = 0$)

$$y_0' = \frac{1}{2h}(y_1 - y_{-1}) = C, \quad y_N = D \tag{6.11}$$

Here a fictitious station x_{-1} (at $x_0 - h$) has been introduced. In this case we need to include x_{-1} in our model of the differential equation, and this may be achieved by applying (6.7) at the left end point x_0 ($i = 0$) as well as at all interior points ($i = 1, 2, \ldots, N-1$). Thus (6.7) ($i = 0, \ldots, N-1$) and (6.11) constitute $N+2$ linear equations for $y_{-1}, y_0, \ldots, y_N$. If we prefer we may substitute for y_{-1} ($= y_1 - 2hC$) in (6.7) to give $N+1$ equations for $y_0, \ldots, y_N$.

6.3 Solution of three-term recurrence relations (tridiagonal systems)

The set of equations (6.7) for $y_0, \ldots, y_N$ ($i = 1, \ldots, N-1$) with boundary conditions (6.9) [and similarly the set of equations (6.7), (6.11)] may be solved by standard matrix methods, as in Reference 1. For example, Gauss elimination might be considered, or even more simply (if they are available) BASIC matrix routines might be adopted. Indeed, we use this simple approach in Section 6.4. (See (6.22) for the form of these equations.)

However, (6.7) is a set of three-term recurrence relations with boundary values (6.9), and such equations may be solved by a much simpler and more efficient procedure. Suppose (6.7), (6.9) are rewritten

$$u_i y_{i-1} + v_i y_i + w_i y_{i+1} = s_i \quad (i = 1, \ldots, N-1) \tag{6.12}$$

where

$$y_0 = C, \quad y_N = D \quad \text{(given)} \tag{6.13}$$

and

$$u_i = \frac{p_i}{h^2} - \frac{q_i}{2h}, \quad v_i = -\frac{2p_i}{h^2} + r_i, \quad w_i = \frac{p_i}{h^2} + \frac{q_i}{2h} \tag{6.14}$$

Then we may first of all seek a solution $y_0^{(1)}, y_1^{(1)}, \ldots, y_N^{(1)}$ of the *homogeneous* (initial-value) problem

$$u_i y_{i-1}^{(1)} + v_i y_i^{(1)} + w_i y_{i+1}^{(1)} = 0 \tag{6.15}$$

subject to

$$y_0^{(1)} = 0, \quad y_1^{(1)} = 1 \tag{6.15a}$$

This solution may be computed explicitly from (6.15) by determining

$$y_{i+1}^{(1)} = -(u_i y_{i-1}^{(1)} + v_i y_i^{(1)})/w_i \quad (i = 1, 2, \ldots, N-1) \tag{6.16}$$

The second step is to determine the *particular solution* $y_0^{(2)}, y_1^{(2)}, \ldots, y_N^{(2)}$ of the given *non-homogeneous* equation (6.12), namely

$$u_i y_{i-1}^{(2)} + v_i y_i^{(2)} + w_i y_{i+1}^{(2)} = s_i \tag{6.17}$$

$$y_0^{(2)} = C, \quad y_1^{(2)} = 0 \tag{6.18}$$

This simply involves computing explicitly from (6.16), using

$$y_{i+1}^{(2)} = (s_i - u_i y_{i-1}^{(2)} - v_i y_i^{(2)})/w_i \quad (i = 1, \ldots, N-1) \tag{6.19}$$

The solution of (6.12), (6.13) that we actually require is now found by taking y_i $(i = 0, \ldots, N)$ to be a linear combination of $y_i^{(1)}, y_i^{(2)}$, namely

$$y_i = \lambda y_i^{(1)} + y_i^{(2)} \quad \text{(for some parameter } \lambda) \tag{6.20}$$

Once the appropriate λ has been selected, then (6.20) determines the solution of (6.12), (6.13). First, by adding λ times (6.15) to (6.17), we deduce that

$$u_i[\lambda y_{i-1}^{(1)} + y_{i-1}^{(2)}] + v_i[\lambda y_i^{(1)} + y_i^{(2)}] + w_i[\lambda y_{i+1}^{(1)} + y_{i+1}^{(2)}] = 0 + s_i$$

Hence

$$u_i y_{i-1} + v_i y_i + w_i y_{i+1} = s_i$$

and $\{y_i\}$ satisfies (6.12). Secondly, as required,

$$y_0 = \lambda y_0^{(1)} + y_0^{(2)} = \lambda 0 + C = C$$

Finally, if we apply the remaining condition $y_N = D$ from (6.13), we deduce that

$$y_N = \lambda y_N^{(1)} + y_N^{(2)} = D$$

Thus

$$\lambda = (D - y_N^{(2)})/y_N^{(1)} \qquad (6.21)$$

and the appropriate value of λ is known.

If the set of equations (6.12) are set out in matrix form, then we obtain

$$
\begin{pmatrix}
1 & 0 & & & & 0 \\
u_1 & v_1 & w_1 & & & \\
 & u_2 & v_2 & w_2 & & \\
 & & & \cdot & & \\
 & & & & \cdot & \\
 & & u_{N-1} & v_{N-1} & w_{N-1} \\
0 & & & 0 & 1
\end{pmatrix}
\begin{pmatrix}
y_0 \\ y_1 \\ y_2 \\ \cdot \\ \cdot \\ \cdot \\ y_{N-1} \\ y_N
\end{pmatrix}
=
\begin{pmatrix}
s_0 \\ s_1 \\ s_2 \\ \cdot \\ \cdot \\ \cdot \\ s_{N-1} \\ s_N
\end{pmatrix}
\qquad (6.22)
$$

The matrix on the left has entries only on its main diagonal and the adjacent diagonals (giving three adjacent entries per row)), and so it is termed a *tridiagonal matrix*. In the above discussion we have thus given an efficient algorithm for solving 'tridiagonal systems' of linear equations.

Just how efficient is our procedure above compared with general matrix techniques? In Reference 1 we saw the solution of $N+1$ equations by Gauss elimination involved $O((N+1)^3)$ arithmetic operations. In contrast it is not difficult to see that the present procedure ((6.15a), (6.16), (6.18), (6.19), (6.20), (6.21)) involves $O(N+1)$ arithmetic operations.

We now formalize the solution procedure in the following algorithm.

Algorithm 6.0 Solution of a three-term recurrence/tridiagonal system

The solution of (6.12), (6.13) (given $u_i, v_i, w_i, s_i, C, D, N$) is determined as follows:

    (i) Calculate $y_i^{(1)}(i = 0, 1, \ldots, N)$ from (6.15a), (6.16).
    (ii) Calculate $y_i^{(2)}(i = 0, 1, \ldots, N)$ from (6.18), (6.19).

(iii) Determine λ from (6.21).
(iv) Calculate $y_i (i = 0, 1, \ldots, N)$ from (6.20).

We shall not give a program here for Algorithm 6.0 (hence its numbering!), since in particular an input specification for u_i, v_i, w_i, s_i is tedious. Instead we shall incorporate the algorithm in future programs in which u_i, v_i, w_i, s_i are already calculated.

6.4 Beam bending problems

Let us consider a simple problem and develop a corresponding program, so as to illustrate and use the above ideas. The equation of beam bending gives

$$EIy'' = M(x) \tag{6.23}$$

Let us assume that E and I are constant at all points x of the beam, and let us first consider the case of a light beam which is centrally loaded (with load P) and simply supported (see *Figure 6.1*).
  In this case the bending moment is clearly

$$M(x) = \begin{cases} -Px/2 & (0 \leqslant x \leqslant l/2) \\ -P(l-x)/2 & (l/2 < x \leqslant l) \end{cases} \tag{6.24}$$

Choose $N+1$ stations $x_0, \ldots, x_N$ equally spaced by $h = l/N$ and let y_i denote $y(x_i)$ as usual. Then (6.23), (6.24) are modelled at $x = x_i$, according to Section 6.2, by

$$\frac{EI}{h^2}(y_{i+1} - 2y_i + y_{i-1}) = M(x_i) = \begin{cases} -Pil/2N & (x_i \leqslant l/2) \\ -P(N-i)l/2N & (x_i > l/2) \end{cases} \tag{6.25}$$

The corresponding boundary conditions give

$$y_0 = y_N = 0 \tag{6.26}$$

For example, if we adopt a crude model with $N = 4$ ($h = l/4$) then we obtain from (6.25) three simultaneous equations:

$$\left. \begin{array}{l} y_0 - 2y_1 + y_2 = -\dfrac{l^2}{16EI} \dfrac{Pl}{8} = -\dfrac{Pl^3}{128EI} \times 1 \\[4mm] y_1 - 2y_2 + y_3 = -\dfrac{l^2}{16EI} \dfrac{Pl}{4} = -\dfrac{Pl^3}{128EI} \times 2 \\[4mm] y_2 - 2y_3 + y_4 = -\dfrac{l^2}{16EI} \dfrac{Pl}{8} = -\dfrac{Pl^3}{128EI} \times 1 \end{array} \right\} \tag{6.27}$$

Using (6.26) we deduce that

$$\begin{pmatrix} -2 & 1 & 0 \\ 1 & -2 & 1 \\ 0 & 1 & -2 \end{pmatrix} \begin{pmatrix} y_1 \\ y_2 \\ y_3 \end{pmatrix} = \frac{-Pl^3}{128EI} \begin{pmatrix} 1 \\ 2 \\ 1 \end{pmatrix} \tag{6.28}$$

Thus

$$\begin{pmatrix} y_1 \\ y_2 \\ y_3 \end{pmatrix} = \frac{-Pl^3}{128EI} \begin{pmatrix} -2 & 1 & 0 \\ 1 & -2 & 1 \\ 0 & 1 & -2 \end{pmatrix}^{-1} \begin{pmatrix} 1 \\ 2 \\ 1 \end{pmatrix} \tag{6.29}$$

and the solution may be determined (in principle) by matrix methods. However, for this simple case, if we write

$$y_i = -\frac{Pl^3}{128EI} y_i^* \tag{6.30}$$

then (6.27) gives

$$-2y_1^* + y_2^* = 1, \quad y_1^* - 2y_2^* + y_3^* = 2, \quad y_2^* - 2y_3^* = 1$$

Substituting for y_1^*, y_3^* from the first and third equations in the second equation:

$$\tfrac{1}{2}(y_2^* - 1) - 2y_2^* + \tfrac{1}{2}(y_2^* - 1) = 2$$

Hence

$$y_2^* = -3 \quad \text{and} \quad y_1^* = y_3^* = -2$$

From (6.30) we deduce that

$$y_0 = 0, \quad y_1 = \frac{Pl^3}{64EI}, \quad y_2 = \frac{3Pl^3}{128EI}, \quad y_3 = \frac{Pl^3}{64EI}, \quad y_4 = 0$$

For the general case (N unspecified), (6.25) gives

$$y_{i-1} - 2y_i + y_{i+1} = s_i \quad (i = 1, 2, \ldots, N) \tag{6.31}$$

where

$$s_i = -\frac{l^2}{N^2 EI} \frac{Pl}{2N} \begin{cases} i & (x_i \leqslant l/2) \\ N - i & (x_i > l/2) \end{cases} \tag{6.32}$$

In fact s_i relates simply to the function $s(x)$, defined by

$$s(x) = M(x)/(EI) \quad \text{and} \quad s_i = s(x_i) \tag{6.33}$$

Substituting $y_0 = y_N = 0$ in (6.31), we may rewrite the equations in matrix form as

$$\mathbf{Ay} = \mathbf{s} \tag{6.34}$$

where

$$A = \begin{pmatrix} -2 & 1 & & & & 0 \\ 1 & -2 & 1 & & & \\ & 1 & -2 & 1 & & \\ & & \ddots & & & \\ & & & \ddots & & \\ & & & \ddots & & \\ 0 & & 1 & -2 & 1 \\ & & & 1 & -2 \end{pmatrix}, y = \begin{pmatrix} y_1 \\ y_2 \\ \cdot \\ \cdot \\ \cdot \\ y_{N-1} \end{pmatrix}, s = \begin{pmatrix} s_1 \\ s_2 \\ \cdot \\ \cdot \\ \cdot \\ s_{N-1} \end{pmatrix} \quad (6.35)$$

In the following algorithm and program, the system (6.34) is solved by BASIC matrix routines.

Algorithm 6.1   Beam bending by matrix routines

Choose N, h and corresponding stations x_i.
Define the function $s(x)$ given by (6.33), and hence the values s_i.
Generate the matrix A given by (6.35).
Calculate the vector s given by (6.35).
Calculate the vector $y = A^{-1}s$ by BASIC matrix routines.

Program 6.1   BEAMMAT: Beam bending by matrix routines

```
LIST
BEAMMAT

10      REM- BEAMMAT: SOLN OF SIMPLY SUPPORTED BEAM PROBLEM
20      REM- (EIY''=M) USING CENTRAL DIFFERENCES. LINEAR
30      REM- EQUATIONS SOLVED BY BASIC MATRIX ROUTINES.
40      DIM A(40,40),B(40,40),S(40,1),X(40),Y(40,1)
50      PRINT "LOAD";
60      INPUT P
70      PRINT "YOUNG'S MODULUS";
80      INPUT E
90      PRINT "NO OF STATIONS";
100     INPUT N
110     PRINT "BEAM LENGTH";
120     INPUT L
130     DEF FNI(X)=1
140     DEF FNM(X,L,P)=-.5*P*(.5*L-ABS(X-.5*L))
150     H=L/N
160     X(0)=0
170     N1=N-1
180     MAT A=ZER(N1,N1)
190     MAT S=ZER(N1,1)
200     MAT Y=ZER(N1,1)
210     FOR I=1 TO N1
220     X(I)=X(I-1)+H
230     S(I,1)=H*H*FNM(X(I),L,P)/(E*FNI(X(I)))
240     A(I,I)=-2
250     IF I=1 THEN 270
260     A(I,I-1)=1
270     IF I=N1 THEN 290
280     A(I,I+1)=1
290     NEXT I
```

```
300    MAT B=INV(A)
310    MAT Y= B*S
320    PRINT "X VALUE:","DISPLACEMENT:"
330    FOR I=1 TO N1
340    PRINT X(I),Y(I,1)
350    NEXT I
360    END

Ready
```

Sample run 1

```
RUN
BEAMMAT

LOAD? 100
YOUNG'S MODULUS? 1
NO OF STATIONS? 10
BEAM LENGTH? 1
X VALUE:        DISPLACEMENT:
 .1              .625
 .2             1.2
 .3             1.675
 .4             2
 .5             2.125
 .6             2
 .7             1.675
 .8             1.2
 .9              .625
Ready
```

Sample run 2

```
RUN
BEAMMAT

LOAD? 100
YOUNG'S MODULUS? 1
NO OF STATIONS? 20
BEAM LENGTH? 1
X VALUE:        DISPLACEMENT:
 .05             .3125
 .1              .61875
 .15             .9125
 .2             1.1875
 .25            1.4375
 .3             1.65625
 .35            1.8375
 .4             1.975
 .45            2.0625
 .5             2.09375
 .55            2.0625
 .6             1.975
 .65            1.8375
 .7             1.65625
 .75            1.4375
 .8             1.1875
 .85             .9125
 .9              .61875
 .95             .3125
Ready
```

Sample run 3

```
RUN
BEAMMAT

LOAD? 100
YOUNG'S MODULUS? 1
NO OF STATIONS? 40
BEAM LENGTH? 1
X VALUE:        DISPLACEMENT:
 .025            .15625
 .05             .311719
 .075            .465625
 .1              .617188
 .125            .765626
 .15             .910157
 .175           1.05
 .2             1.18438
 .225           1.3125
 .25            1.4336
 .275           1.54688
 .3             1.65156
 .325           1.74688
 .35            1.83203
 .375           1.90625
 .4             1.96875
 .425           2.01875
 .45            2.05547
 .475           2.07813
 .5             2.08594
 .525           2.07813
 .55            2.05547
 .575           2.01875
 .6             1.96875
 .625           1.90625
 .65            1.83203
 .675           1.74688
 .7             1.65156
 .725           1.54688
 .75            1.4336
 .775           1.3125
 .8             1.18438
 .825           1.05
 .85             .910157
 .875            .765626
 .9              .617188
 .925            .465626
 .95             .311719
 .975            .15625
Ready
```

Program notes

(1) The program does not use dynamic dimensioning. Fixed dimensions are, in particular, given to the matrices A,S,Y in line 40. These dimensions are then reduced from 40 to $(N-1)$ (in one or both indices) by the instructions 180, 190, 200.

(2) The vectors S and Y are represented as $(N-1)$ by 1 matrices, in order to make use of matrix multiplications in instruction 310.
(3) The second moment of area, $I(x)$, is defined by FNI(X).

The bending moment $M(x)$ is defined by FNM(X,L,P) according to the formula (6.24), where X is the distance, L is the beam length, and P is the load. In fact (6.24) is replaced by the single (equivalent) formula

$$M(x) = \frac{-P}{2}(\tfrac{1}{2}l - |x - \tfrac{1}{2}l|)$$

(4) Three sample runs are given, each for $P = 100$ and $E = I = 1$, but with $n = 10$, 20, and 40 stations respectively. Note that the displacement at $x = 0.5$ is computed as

2.125, 2.09375, 2.08594   for $n = 10$, 20, 40

If Richardson h^2-extrapolation is applied (see Section 6.6 below) to the pair of values 2.125, 2.09375, then an improved estimate is obtained, namely *2.08333*. If h^2-extrapolation is applied to the pair 2.09375, 2.08594, then the improved estimate is *2.08334*. We can therefore predice a central deflection to five significant figures (at least). The value 2.08594, obtained for $n = 40$, was correct to within 0.1 per cent.

The above program is inefficient and we now illustrate the use of Algorithm 6.0 in the following alternative algorithm and program (for the same centrally loaded and simply supported beam problem).

Algorithm 6.2 Beam bending by three-term recurrence relations

Choose N, h and stations x_i.
Define the function $s(x)$ by (6.33) and hence the values s_i.
Define $u_i = w_i = 1$, $v_i = -2$ for every i, $C = D = 0$.
Calculate y_i $(i = 0, \ldots, N)$ from Algorithm 6.0.

Program 6.2   BEAMREC: Beam bending by three-term recurrence

```
LIST
    10REM   BEAMREC: SOLN OF SIMPLY SUP-
    20REM-  PORTED BEAM PROBLEM (E1Y  =M)
    30REM-  USING CENTRAL DIFFERENCES. THE
    40REM-  RECURRENCE RELATIONS SOLVED
    50REM-  BY SUPERPOSING 2 SOLUTIONS.
    60DIM  X(64),Y(64),Y1(64),Y2(64)
    70PRINT  "LOAD";
    80INPUT  P
    90PRINT  "YOUNG'S MODULUS";
   100INPUT  E
   110PRINT  "NO OF STNS";
```

```
120INPUT N
130PRINT "BEAM LENGTH";
140INPUT L
150DEF FNI(X)=1
160DEF FNM(X,L,P)=-.5*P*(.5*L-ABS(X-.5*L))
170H=L/N
180X(0)=0
190Y1(0)=0
200Y1(1)=1
210Y2(0)=0
220Y2(1)=0
230N1=N-1
240FOR I=1 TO N1
250X(I)=X(I-1)+H
260S=FNM(X(I),L,P)/(E*FNI(X(I)))
270Y1(I+1)=2*Y1(I)-Y1(I-1)
280Y2(I+1)=2*Y2(I)-Y2(I-1)+S*H*H
290NEXT I
300LAM =-Y2(N)/Y1(N)
310PRINT "X VALUE","   DISPLACEMT"
320FOR I=0 TO N
330Y(I)=LAM*Y1(I)+Y2(I)
340PRINT X(I),"   ";Y(I)
350NEXT I
360END
>
```

Sample run

```
RUN
LOAD?100
YOUNG'S MODULUS?1
NO OF STNS?40
BEAM LENGTH?1
X VALUE        DISPLACEMT
        0      0
2.5E-2         0.15625
  5E-2         0.311718749
7.5E-2         0.465624999
   0.1         0.617187499
 0.125         0.765624998
 0.15          0.910156248
 0.175         1.05
 0.2           1.184375
 0.225         1.3125
 0.25          1.43359375
 0.275         1.546875
 0.3           1.6515625
 0.325         1.746875
 0.35          1.83203125
 0.375         1.90624999
 0.4           1.96874999
 0.425         2.01874999
 0.45          2.05546874
 0.475         2.07812499
 0.5           2.08593749
 0.525         2.07812499
 0.55          2.05546874
 0.575         2.01874999
 0.6           1.96874999
 0.625         1.90624999
 0.65          1.83203124 .
 0.675         1.74687499
0.699999999         1.65156249
0.724999999         1.54687499
0.749999999         1.43359374
0.774999999         1.31249999
0.799999999         1.18437499
0.824999999         1.04999999
0.849999999         0.910156243
0.874999999         0.765624993
0.899999999         0.617187494
0.924999999         0.465624996
0.949999999         0.311718747
0.974999998         0.156249998
        0      0
```

Program notes

(1) The variables $y_i^{(1)}, y_i^{(2)}$ are represented in the program by Y1(I) and Y2(I).
(2) The single variable S is used to represent $s_i = s(x_i)$.
(3) In the Sample run, the case $P = 100$, $E = I = 1$, $n = 40$ is considered, and essentially the same results are obtained as in Program 6.1. (Note that two different computers of different precisions have been used for the two programs.)

6.4.1 Other problems for simply supported beams

In the example above we consider a light centrally loaded beam. However, Programs 6.1, 6.2 may readily be applied to other problems for simply supported beams: the only change that is normally required to the programs being in the definitions of $I(x)$ and $M(x)$.

Consider first a heavy uniform beam of weight w per unit length. This is illustrated in *Figure 6.2*, and it is easy to deduce that $I(x) = 1$ and that

$$M(x) = \frac{-wl}{2}x + \frac{wx}{2}x = \frac{-wx}{2}(l - x)$$

Letting P perform the role of w, we write

160 DEF FNM(X,L,P) = $-$P*X*(L$-$X)*.5

Tapered beams, in which either the second moment of area $I(x)$ or the

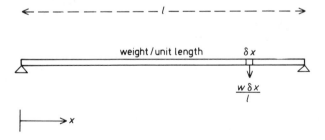

Figure 6.2. Simply supported, heavy uniform beam.

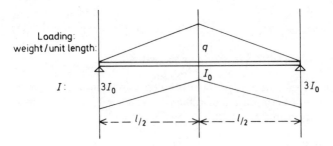

Figure 6.3. Doubly tapered, simply supported beam.

weight per unit length are variable, are also readily dealt with. For example, for the doubly tapered beam of *Figure 6.3* it is easy to see that

$$I(x) = \begin{cases} (3l - 4x)I_0/l & x \leqslant l/2 \\ (4x - l)I_0/l & x > l/2 \end{cases}$$

In this case $M(x)$ is a little more difficult to determine. The weight of the rod per unit length at position x is $qx/(\frac{1}{2}l)$. Thus the weight of each half rod (of length $l/2$) is

$$\int_0^{l/2} (qx)/(\tfrac{1}{2}l)\, \mathrm{d}x = ql/4$$

and acts one-third of the way along. Hence we obtain

$$x \leqslant l/2: \; M(x) = -\frac{ql}{4}x + \frac{qx}{\frac{1}{2}l}\frac{x}{2}\frac{x}{3} = \frac{-qx}{12l}(3l^2 - 4x^2)$$

$$x > l/2: \; M(x) = \frac{-q(l-x)}{12l}[3l^2 - 4(l-x)^2]$$

The reader is left to implement these formulae by appropriate changes to the definition statements.

In all the above problems we have taken $E = 1$. Moreover, we have taken $I = 1$ for uniform inertia problems. This does not represent any loss of generality, and we need only divide the resulting solutions by the true values of E and I to obtain the required solution (since this set of y values is proportional to $1/(EI)$).

6.5 General two-point boundary-value problems

In the last section we developed algorithms for the problem (6.1) of beam bending, so as to provide simple and specific examples of the central difference method. Let us now broaden the (recurrence relation) approach of Algorithm 6.2 to cover the general two-point boundary-value problem (6.5), namely

$$p(x)y'' + q(x)y' + r(x)y = s(x) \quad (a \leqslant x \leqslant b) \tag{6.36}$$

and let us first consider the elementary boundary conditions (compare (6.8))

$$y(a) = C, \quad y(b) = D \tag{6.37}$$

All necessary steps in the central difference approximation method have already been given above in earlier discussions. We may therefore immediately propose the following algorithm and program.

Algorithm 6.3 Solution of two-point boundary-value problem with elementary end conditions, by recurrence

Choose N, h and stations x_i.
Define the functions $p(x)$, $q(x)$, $r(x)$ and $s(x)$ in (6.36).
Define the interval $[a, b]$ and end conditions C and D in (6.37).
Evaluate p_i, q_i, r_i, s_i and hence determine u_i, v_i, w_i from (6.14).
Calculate y_i $(i = 0, \ldots, N)$ from Algorithm 6.0.

Program 6.3   BVPREC: Solution of general two-point boundary-value problem

```
LIST
   10REM- BVPREC: SOLN OF GENERAL 2-PT     320F=P/(H*H)
   20REM- LINEAR BOUNDARY VALUE PROBLEM    330G=.5*Q/H
   30REM- P(X)Y''+Q(X)Y'+R(X)Y=S(X),       340U=F-G
   40REM- Y(A)=C,    Y(B)=D                 350V=R-2*F
   50REM- USING CENTRAL DIFFERENCES,        360W=F+G
   60REM- RECURRENCE SOLVED BY SUPER-       370IF I=N THEN 400
   70REM- POSITION.                         380Y1(I+1)=-(U*Y1(I-1)+V*Y1(I))/W
   80DIM X(64),Y1(64),Y2(64),Y(64)          390Y2(I+1)=(S-U*Y2(I-1)-V*Y2(I))/W
   90PRINT "END PTS A,B";                    400NEXT I
  100INPUT A,B                               410LAM=(D-Y2(N))/Y1(N)
  110PRINT "BOUNDARY VALUES C,D";            420PRINT "X VALUES","    SOLUTIONS"
  120INPUT C,D                               430FOR I=0 TO N
  130PRINT "NO OF STATIONS N";               440Y(I)=LAM*Y1(I)+Y2(I)
  140INPUT N                                 450PRINT X(I),"   ";Y(I)
  150DEF FNP(X)=(X+1)*(X+2)                  460NEXT I
  160DEF FNQ(X)=4*X+6                        470END
  170DEF FNR(X)=2
  180DEF FNS(X)=EXP(X)
  190Y1(0)=0
  200Y1(1)=1
  210Y2(0)=C
  220Y2(1)=0
  230X(0)=A
  240H=(B-A)/N
  250N1=N-1
  260FOR I=1 TO N
  270X(I)=X(I-1)+H
  280P=FNP(X(I))
  290Q=FNQ(X(I))
  300R=FNR(X(I))
  310S=FNS(X(I))
```

118 Boundary-value problems

Sample run 1

```
RUN
END PTS A,B?0,1
BOUNDARY VALUES C,D?1,.7863803
NO OF STATIONS N?10
X VALUES        SOLUTIONS
        0       1.
        0.1     0.954539153
        0.2     0.91708434
        0.3     0.88612
        0.4     0.860549844
        0.5     0.839562728
        0.6     0.822548059
        0.7     0.809040496
        0.8     0.79868271
        0.9     0.791199636
        1       0.7863803
>
```

```
RUN
END PTS A,B?0,1
BOUNDARY VALUES C,D?1,.7863803
NO OF STATIONS N?20
X VALUES        SOLUTIONS
        0       1
        5E-2    0.976188378
        0.1     0.954599430
        0.15    0.934993652
        0.2     0.917169677
        0.25    0.900957024
        0.3     0.886210379
        0.35    0.872805184
        0.4     0.860634111
        0.45    0.849604279
        0.5     0.839631988
        0.55    0.830655916
        0.6     0.822640509
        0.65    0.815430183
        0.7     0.809082491
        0.75    0.803521065
0.800000001             0.798780521
0.850000001             0.794615932
0.900000001             0.791212318
0.950000001             0.788474211
        1       0.7863803
```

Sample run 2

```
>150    DEF FNP(X)=1
>160    DEF FNQ(X)=-2
>170    DEF FNR(X)=1
>180    DEF FNS(X)=X
.RUN
END PTS A,B?0,1
BOUNDARY VALUES C,D?2,5.7182818
NO OF STATIONS N?20
X VALUES        SOLUTIONS
        0       2
        5E-2    2.10251644
        0.1     2.21042273
        0.15    2.32413383
        0.2     2.44409311
        0.25    2.57077418
        0.3     2.70468279
        0.35    2.84635894
        0.4     2.99637898
        0.45    3.15535803
        0.5     3.32395235
        0.55    3.50286199
        0.6     3.69283353
        0.65    3.89466301
        0.7     4.10919912
        0.75    4.33734642
0.800000001             4.58006883
0.850000001             4.83839342
0.900000001             5.11341426
0.950000001             5.4062967
        1       5.71828181
>
```

```
.RUN
END PTS A,B?0,1
BOUNDARY VALUES C,D?2,5.7182818
NO OF STATIONS N?40
X VALUES        SOLUTIONS
        0       2
        2.5E-2  2.05062701
        5E-2    2.10255179
        7.5E-2  2.15582365
        0.1     2.21049354
        0.125   2.26661412
        0.15    2.32423986
        0.175   2.38342702
        0.2     2.44423376
        0.225   2.50672018
        0.25    2.57094839
        0.275   2.63698258
        0.3     2.70488905
        0.325   2.77473632
        0.35    2.84659515
        0.375   2.92053866
        0.4     2.9966424
        0.425   3.07498431
        0.45    3.15564503
        0.475   3.23870783
        0.5     3.32425863
        0.525   3.41238624
        0.55    3.50318235
        0.575   3.59674153
        0.6     3.69316158
        0.625   3.79254353
        0.65    3.89499152
        0.675   4.00061318
0.699999999             4.10951954
0.724999999             4.22182524
0.749999999             4.33764863
0.774999999             4.45711195
0.799999999             4.58034122
0.824999999             4.70746678
0.849999999             4.83862287
0.874999999             4.973948
0.899999999             5.11358547
0.924999999             5.25768274
0.949999999             5.40639228
0.974999998             5.55987126
0.999999998             5.71828181
>
```

Sample run 3

```
150     DEF FNP(X)=-50              RUN
>160    DEF FNQ(X)=0.1              END PTS A,B?0,20
>170    DEF FNR(X)=0.00001          BOUNDARY VALUES C,D?1,0
>180    DEF FNS(X)=0                NO OF STATIONS N?16
>255    NH=INT(.5*N+.5)             X VALUES        SOLUTIONS
>312    IF I <> NH THEN 320                 0       1
                                        1.25        0.939902545
>314    S=0.1/H                         2.5         0.879654953
>RUN                                    3.75        0.8.9256829
END P1S A,B?0,20                        5           0.758707776
BOUNDARY VALUES C,D?1,0                 6.25        0.698007399
NO OF STATIONS N?8                      7.5         0.637155302
X VALUES        SOLUTIONS               8.75        0.57615108
        0       1                       10          0.514994342
        2.5     0.879654975             11.25       0.451181553
        5       0.75870782              12.5        0.387209177
        7.5     0.637155362             13.75       0.323076796
        10      0.514994418             15          0.258783985
        12.5    0.387209252             16.25       0.194330323
        15      0.258784041             17.5        0.129715387
        17.5    0.12971542              18.75       6.49387538E-2
        20      0                       20          0
>
```

Program notes

(1) The program variables P,Q,R,S,U,V,W are used for $p_i, q_i, r_i, s_i, u_i, v_i, w_i$.

(2) In the original program and Sample run 1, we solve the differential equation

$$(x+1)(x+2)y'' + (4x+6)y' + 2y = e^x$$

subject to $y(0) = 1$, $y(1) = (e+2)/6 = 0.7863803$. The true solution is

$$y = (e^x + x + 1)/[(x+1)(x+2)]$$

At $x = 0.5$, this true solution is $y = 0.8396590$.
The computed solutions for $n = 10$, 20 at $x = 0.5$ are

0.8395627,   0.8396350

Richardson h^2-extrapolation (Section 6.6 below) of the latter two values leads to the improved estimate 0.8396591 (correct to nearly seven figures!).

(3) In Sample run 2, new functions FNP, FNQ, FNR, FNS are defined to correspond to the differential equation

$$y'' - 2y' + y = x$$

with boundary conditions $y(0) = 2$, $y(1) = 3 + e = 5.7182818$.
The true solution is $y = e^{x+x} + 2$, and, at $x = 0.5$, $y = 3.324361$.
The computed solutions for $n = 20$, 40 at $x = 0.5$ are 3.323952, 3.324259.

Richardson h^2-extrapolation of these two values gives the improved value 3.324361 (correct to seven figures!).

(4) In Sample run 3, we solve a river pollution problem (Section 6.5.1

below) with new functions FNP,... chosen to correspond to the equation

$$-50y'' + 0.1y' + 0.00001y = S(x)$$

where $S = 0.1/h$ at $x = 10$ and zero otherwise, for $y(0) = 1$, $y(20) = 0$.

Assuming N (the number of stations) is even (so that $x = 10$ is a station), we choose $S = 0.1/h$ at $I = NH = N/2$ and zero otherwise.

The program is run for $N = 8, 16$ and accurate results can be seen to be obtained.

6.5.1 A river pollution problem

A model problem which fits into the form (6.36), (6.37) required for Program 6.3, but with $p(x), q(x)$ and $r(x)$ fixed as constants, is that of pollution and tidal mixing in a river estuary. In this case $y(x)$ is the concentration of pollutant (say salt) (in $kg\,m^{-3}$) at distance x, p is the diffusion coefficient (due to tidal mixing) (in $m^2\,s^{-1}$), q is the mean velocity (in $m\,s^{-1}$), r is the decay constant (i.e. the reciprocal of the time to decay to $1/e$ times the initial value) (in s^{-1}) and s is the rate of increase of y due to a source of pollution inflow (in $kg\,m^{-3}\,s^{-1}$), $h = $ step, and $A = $ cross-sectional area.

The boundary conditions in the problem to conform with (6.36), are the concentrations C and D at the two ends a and b of the estuary. For example, suppose $-p = 50\,m^2\,s^{-1}$, $q = 0.1\,s^{-1}$, and $r = 1/10^5$ (i.e. decay time of 10^5 s). Assume also that salt pollutant discharges at $100\,kg\,s^{-1}$ halfway down an estuary of length 20 km and cross section $1000\,m^2$, and that the salt concentration is $1\,kg\,m^{-3}$ at the sea end and 0 at the inland end. Then the remaining parameters of the problem are

$$s_i = \begin{cases} 100/(1000h) & \text{at } x_i = 10 \\ 0 & \text{otherwise} \end{cases}$$

$$y(0) = 1, \quad y(20) = 0 \text{ (i.e. } a, b, C, D = 0, 20, 1, 0)$$

This problem was solved in Sample run 3 of Program 6.3.

6.5.2. A derivative boundary condition

Suppose that we wish to solve (6.36) with the modified 'mixed' boundary conditions

$$y'(a) = C, \quad y(b) = D$$

Then, from (6.11) above, these conditions become (approximately)

$$y_0' = \frac{1}{2h}(y_1 - y_{-1}) = C \quad \text{and} \quad y_N = D$$

Thus

$$y_{-1} = y_1 - 2hC \tag{6.38}$$

Equation (6.12) (the model of (6.36)) applied at $x = a$ (i.e. $i = 0$) gives

$$u_0 y_{-1} + v_0 y_0 + w_0 y_1 = s_0 \tag{6.39}$$

Substituting (6.38) into (6.39), we obtain

$$v_0 y_0 + (u_0 + w_0)y_1 = s_0 + 2hCu_0 \tag{6.40}$$

Let us assume that $u_0 + w_0 \neq 0$. The equation (6.40) for y_0, y_1 is then added to (6.12), namely

$$u_i y_{i-1} + v_i y_i + w_i y_{i+1} = s_i \quad (i = 1, \ldots, N-1) \tag{6.41}$$

where

$$y_N = D \tag{6.42}$$

to give a set of $N + 1$ equations (6.40)–(6.42) for $y_0, y_1 \ldots, y_N$.

We may solve the tridiagonal system (6.40)–(6.42) efficiently by the type of technique discussed in Section 6.3. Determine $y_1^{(1)}, \ldots y_N^{(1)}$ from

$$u_i y_{i-1}^{(1)} + v_i y_i^{(1)} + w_i y_{i+1}^{(1)} = 0 \quad (i = 1, \ldots, N-1)$$
$$y_0^{(1)} = 1, \quad v_0 y_0^{(1)} + (u_0 + w_0)y_1^{(1)} = 0 \tag{6.43}$$

and $y_2^{(2)}, \ldots, y_N^{(2)}$ from

$$u_i y_{i-1}^{(2)} + v_i y_i^{(2)} + w_i y_{i+1}^{(2)} = s_i \tag{6.43a}$$
$$y_0^{(2)} = 0, \quad v_0 y_0^{(2)} + (u_0 + w_0)y_1^{(2)} = s_0 + 2hCu_0 \tag{6.44}$$

Combine these solutions to obtain

$$y_i = \lambda y_i^{(1)} + y_i^{(2)} \quad \text{(for some } \lambda) \tag{6.45}$$

It follows immediately that y_i satisfies (6.40), (6.41), and also (6.42) provided that

$$\lambda = (D - y_N^{(2)})/y_N^{(1)} \tag{6.46}$$

In fact $y_0 = \lambda$ in this problem. Thus we have the following algorithm.

Algorithm 6.4 Two-point boundary-value problem with $y'(a)$, $y(b)$ given

Choose N, h, and stations x_i.
Define the functions $p(x), q(x), r(x), s(x)$ in (6.36).
Define a, b and $C = y'(a)$, $D = y(b)$.
Evaluate p_i, q_i, r_i, s_i and hence u_i, v_i, w_i from (6.14).
Calculate $y_i^{(1)}, y_i^{(2)}$ ($i = 0, \ldots, N$) from (6.43a), (6.44).
Calculate λ from (6.46).
Determine y_i ($i = 0, \ldots, N$) from (6.45).

Program 6.4   BVPMIX: Two-point mixed boundary-value
problem

```
LIST
BVPMIX

10       REM- BVPMIX: SOLN OF MIXED 2-PT
20       REM- BOUNDARY VALUE PROBLEM
30       REM- P(X)Y'' + Q(X)Y' + R(X)Y = S(X)
40       REM- Y'(A)=C  Y(B)=D
50       REM- USING CENTRAL DIFFERENCES
60       REM- RECURRENCE SOLVED BY SUPER-
70       REM- POSITION.
80       DIM X(64),Y1(64),Y2(64),Y(64)
90       PRINT "END POINTS A,B";
100      INPUT A,B
110      PRINT "BOUNDARY VALUES Y'(A),Y(B)";
120      INPUT C,D
130      PRINT "NUMBER OF STATIONS N";
140      INPUT N
150      DEF FNP(X) = (X+1)*(X+2)
160      DEF FNQ(X) = 4*X+6
170      DEF FNR(X) = 2
180      DEF FNS(X) = EXP(X)
190      Y1(0)=1
210      Y2(0)=0
230      X(0) = A
240      H = (B-A)/N
250      N1 = N-1
260      FOR I=0 TO N
265      IF I=0 THEN 280
270      X(I) = X(I-1) + H
280      P = FNP(X(I))
290      Q = FNQ(X(I))
300      R = FNR(X(I))
310      S = FNS(X(I))
320      F = P/(H*H)
330      G = 0.5*Q/H
340      U = F-G
350      V = R-2*F
360      W = F+G
361      IF I>0 THEN 370
362      Y1(1)=-V/(U+W)
363      Y2(1)=(S+2*H*C*U)/(U+W)
364      GOTO 400
370      IF I=N THEN 400
380      Y1(I+1) = -(U*Y1(I-1)+V*Y1(I))/W
390      Y2(I+1) = (S-U*Y2(I-1)-V*Y2(I))/W
400      NEXT I
410      LAM = (D-Y2(N))/Y1(N)
420      PRINT "X VALUES","   SOLUTIONS"
430      FOR I = 0 TO N
440      Y(I) = LAM*Y1(I)+Y2(I)
450      PRINT X(I),"   ";Y(I)
460      NEXT I
470      END

Ready
```

Sample run 1

```
RUN
BVPMIX

END POINTS A,B? 0,1
BOUNDARY VALUES Y'(A),Y(B)? -.5,0.7863803
NUMBER OF STATIONS N? 10
X VALUES        SOLUTIONS
 0               .997869
 .1              .95288
 .2              .915794
 .3              .885124
 .4              .85979
 .5              .838996
 .6              .822139
 .7              .808763
 .8              .798514
 .9              .791122
 1               .78638
Ready

RUN
BVPMIX

END POINTS A,B? 0,1
BOUNDARY VALUES Y'(A),Y(B)? -.5,0.7863803
NUMBER OF STATIONS N? 20
X VALUES        SOLUTIONS
 0               .999469
 .05             .97572
 .1              .954186
 .15             .934629
 .2              .916848
 .25             .900674
 .3              .885962
 .35             .872588
 .4              .860445
 .45             .84944
 .5              .839494
 .55             .830535
 .6              .822504
 .65             .815345
 .7              .809013
 .75             .803466
 .8              .798667
 .85             .794586
 .9              .791193
 .95             .788465
 1               .78638
Ready
```

Sample run 2

```
150      DEF FNP(X)=1
160      DEF FNQ(X)=-2
170      DEF FNR(X)=1
180      DEF FNS(X)=X
RUN
BVPMIX

END POINTS A,B? 0,0.5
BOUNDARY VALUES Y'(A),Y(B)? 2,3.32436
NUMBER OF STATIONS N? 10
X VALUES        SOLUTIONS
 0               2.00081
 .05             2.10331
 .1              2.21119
 .15             2.32488
 .2              2.4448
 .25             2.57145
 .3              2.70532
 .35             2.84695
 .4              2.99691
 .45             3.15583
 .5              3.32436
Ready
```

```
RUN
BVPMIX

END POINTS A,B? 0,0.5
BOUNDARY VALUES Y'(A),Y(B)? 2,3.32436
NUMBER OF STATIONS N? 20
X VALUES         SOLUTIONS
 0               2.00021
 .025            2.05084
 .05             2.10276
 .075            2.15603
 .1              2.2107
 .125            2.26681
 .15             2.32444
 .175            2.38362
 .2              2.44442
 .225            2.5069
 .25             2.57113
 .275            2.63715
 .3              2.70505
 .325            2.7749
 .35             2.84675
 .375            2.92068
 .4              2.99678
 .425            3.07511
 .45             3.15577
 .475            3.23882
 .5              3.32436
Ready
```

Sample run 3

```
RUN
BVPMIX

END POINTS A,B? 0,1
BOUNDARY VALUES Y'(A),Y(B)? 2,5.7182818
NUMBER OF STATIONS N? 10
X VALUES         SOLUTIONS
 0               3.49748
 .1              3.69999
 .2              3.90751
 .3              4.11994
 .4              4.33714
 .5              4.55887
 .6              4.78476
 .7              5.01435
 .8              5.24703
 .9              5.482
 1               5.71828
Ready
```

Program notes

(1) This program has been written by making the following changes to Program 6.3 (BVPREC):

```
10 REM- BVPMIX: SOLN OF MIXED 2-PT
110 PRINT "BOUNDARY VALUES Y'(A),Y(B)"
190 Y1(0)=1
200 (delete)
210 Y2(0)=0
220 (delete)
260 FOR I=0 TO N
265 IF I=0 THEN 280
```

```
361 IF I > 0 THEN 370
362 Y1(1) = - V/(U + W)
363 Y2(1) = (S + 2*H*C*U)/(U + W)
364 GOTO 400
```

(2) The program is at present set up to solve the equation

$$(x+1)(x+2)y'' + (4x+6)y' + 2y = e^x$$

In Sample run 1, the boundary conditions are specified as

$$y'(0) = -\tfrac{1}{2}, \quad y(1) = (e+2)/6 = 0.7863803$$

corresponding to the true solution $y = (e^x + x + 1)/(x+1)(x+2)$, for which $y(0.5) = 0.8396590$.

Note that the numerical results are very similar to those of Sample run 1 of Program 6.3, which corresponds to the same true y.

(3) In Sample run 2, the equation is changed to

$$y'' - 2y' + y = x$$

with boundary conditions

$$y'(0) = 2, \quad y(0.5) = 0.5\,e^{\frac{1}{2}} + 2.5 = 3.32436\ldots$$

for which the true solution is

$$y = xe^x + x + 2$$

Again good numerical results were obtained.

(4) In Sample run 3, the same equation (as in Sample run 2) is solved, but with boundary conditions

$$y'(0) = 2, \quad y(1) = e + 3 = 5.7182818$$

However, the numerical solution is *not* close to the function

$$y = xe^x + x + 2$$

Why is this? The trouble here is that we have *not* specified a well-posed problem. In fact the two boundary conditions are not independent of each other. The general solution of the differential equation is actually

$$y = (A + Bx)e^x + x + 2$$

and the boundary conditions give respectively

$$y'(0) = 2 \quad \Rightarrow A + B = 1$$
$$y(1) = e + 3 \Rightarrow A + B = 1$$

Thus A and B are not uniquely determined by the two boundary conditions, and there are an infinite number of solutions to the given problem.

The situation becomes worse if we specify, for example,

$$y'(0) = 1 \quad \text{and} \quad y(1) = e + 3$$

since these correspond to the contradictory pair of conditions

$$A + B = 0, \quad A + B = 1$$

and in fact there is *no* solution for the given boundary conditions.

6.6 Richardson extrapolation

It was noted in Section 6.2 that the error in replacing y' and y'' by central difference approximations was $O(h^2)$, and hence it follows that the error in approximating the differential equations at any station x_i is also $O(h^2)$. It is therefore reasonable to assume that

$$y_i = y_i^{\mathrm{T}} + O(h^2) \quad i = 0, 1, \ldots, N \tag{6.47}$$

where y_i^{T}, y_i denote the true and computed values.

Suppose that $y_i^{(1)}, y_i^{(2)}$ are two separate values of y_i computed for two different choices of step h and $h/2$ respectively (the second step being half the first). Then

$$y_i^{(1)} \simeq y_i^{\mathrm{T}} + Ch^2$$

(for some constant C) from (6.47), and

$$y_i^{(2)} \simeq y_i^{\mathrm{T}} + C(h/2)^2$$

Hence

$$y_i^{\mathrm{T}} \simeq \frac{4y_i^{(2)} - y_i^{(1)}}{3} \quad \text{(eliminating } C\text{)} \tag{6.48}$$

In practice this approximation to y_i^{T} is markedly more accurate than either $y_i^{(1)}$ or $y_i^{(2)}$.

6.6.1 Example

Consider the problem

$$y'' - 3y' + 2y = 2, \quad y(0) = 1, \quad y(1) = 2$$

This has the exact solution

$$y(x) = (e^2 - e)^{-1}(e^{2x} - e^x) + 1$$

and

$$y(\tfrac{1}{2}) = 1.2290 \tag{6.49}$$

Now using central differences with $n=2$, $h=\frac{1}{2}$

$$\frac{y_0-2y_1+y_2}{(\frac{1}{2})^2}-3\frac{y_2-y_0}{2(\frac{1}{2})}+2y_1=2$$

Setting $y_0=1$, $y_2=2$, we obtain

$$y(\tfrac{1}{2})=y_1=\ \tfrac{7}{6}=1.1667$$

With $n=4$, $h=\frac{1}{4}$ we obtain

$$\frac{y_0-2y_1+y_2}{(\frac{1}{4})^2}-3\frac{y_2-y_0}{2(\frac{1}{4})}+2y_1=2$$

Hence

$$22y_0-30y_1+10y_2=2$$
$$22y_1-30y_2+10y_3=2$$
$$22y_2-30y_3+10y_4=2$$

Setting $y_0=1$, $y_4=2$ we obtain

$$y(\tfrac{1}{2})=y_2=1.2174$$

Using h^2-extrapolation on the values 1.1667, 1.2174 gives

$$y(\tfrac{1}{2})\simeq\frac{4(1.2174)-1.1667}{3}=1.2343$$

This is a good estimate for the true solution 1.2290 (see (6.49)).

6.7 Non-linear boundary-value problems

So far we have only considered boundary-value problems for linear differential equations, whereas in Chapter 5 we were able to consider initial-value problems for non-linear differential equations. What is the difficulty in considering non-linear problems? If we use a central difference model, as above, then a non-linear differential equation leads to a system of non-linear algebraic equations for the values of y at the stations. Clearly such a system will in general be difficult to solve.

One of the most powerful types of method to use is a 'shooting method'. The idea of such a method is to replace the boundary-value problem by an equivalent initial-value problem. For example, if the given second order non-linear differential equation has associated boundary conditions

$$y(0)=0, \quad y(1)=1 \tag{6.50}$$

then we might seek a value of a parameter λ so that the solution y subject to the initial conditions

$$y(0) = 0, \quad y'(0) = \lambda \tag{6.51}$$

satisfies

$$y(1) = 1 \tag{6.52}$$

In effect the problem reduces to the solution of a single non-linear algebraic equation (6.52) in λ, where each evaluation of the left-hand side in (6.52) involves the solution of a differential equation with given initial conditions (6.51).

Another useful and related technique is a 'continuation method', applied when central difference formulae are adopted in the boundary problem. Suppose that an initial-value solution has already been obtained for $\lambda = 1$ in (6.51) and that this corresponds, say, to

$$y(1) = \alpha$$

Then a succession of boundary-value problems would be solved by central differences for the boundary conditions

$$y(0) = 0, \quad y(1) = C \quad (C = \alpha_1, \alpha_2, \ldots, \alpha_n)$$

where $\alpha_1 = 1$, $\alpha_n = \alpha$. Newton's method would be used to solve each required non-linear algebraic system $(C = \alpha_1, \alpha_2, \ldots)$ based on the solution of the immediately preceding system.

For further details and discussions of non-linear problems, the reader is referred to Reference 2.

6.8 Reference

1. MASON, J.C., *Basic Matrix Methods*, Butterworths (1984)
2. KELLER, H.B., *Numerical Methods for Two-point Boundary-Value Problems*, Ginn-Blaisdell, Waltham, MA (1968)

PROBLEMS

(6.1) Use Program 6.1 or Program 6.2 to determine the displacements (as a function of x) of a simply supported beam in the cases of
 (i) a heavy uniform beam (Figure 6.2)
 (ii) a doubly tapered beam (Figure 6.3)
where ω, p, l, I are taken equal to unity. (See Section 6.4.1 for the derivation of $I(x), M(x)$.)

(6.2) Modify Program 6.1 to deal with the mixed boundary conditions

$$y'(0) = C, \quad y(l) = D$$

as discussed in Section 6.2 (compare Program 6.4). Apply the resulting program to the case of a centrally loaded light beam, supported at one end ($x = l$, $D = 0$) and held horizontally (but free to move vertically) at the other end ($x = 0$, $C = 0$).

(6.3) Use Program 6.3 to solve the problem discussed in Section 6.6, namely

$$y'' - 3y' + 2y = 2; \quad y(0) = 1, \quad y(1) = 2$$

for $n = 10, 20, 40$ stations.

Apply Richardson h^2-extrapolation to the resulting values at $x = 0.5$, and compare the predicted values with the true solution.

(6.4) The equation governing the radial displacement u in a thick cylinder as a function of its radius r is

$$\frac{d^2u}{dr^2} + \frac{1}{r}\frac{du}{dr} - \frac{u}{r^2} = 0$$

and the hoop strain $\varepsilon_\theta = u/r$ is known at the inner and outer radii of the cylinder:

$\varepsilon_\theta = 760$ micro strain at $r = 100$ mm

$\varepsilon_\theta = 257$ micro strain at $r = 200$ mm

Use Program 6.3 to determine the radial displacements and hoop strains throughout the cylinder, for a specified number (N) of divisions ($N = 4, 8, 16$).

(6.5) Use Richardson h^2-extrapolation to improve upon the numerical solutions obtained from Program 6.4 at $x = 0.5$ in Sample run 1 and at $x = 0.25$ in Sample run 2. Compare the predicted values with the true solutions at these points.

(6.6) Modify Program 6.4 to cover the more general mixed conditions

$$\alpha y(a) + \beta y'(a) = C, \quad y(b) = D$$

where α, β are given constants, and test the resulting program on the equation

$$y'' - 2y' + y = x$$

with $y(0) - y'(0) = 0$, $y(1) = e + 3 = 5.7182818$. [The true solution is $y = x e^x + x + 2$.]

(6.7) By determining the general solution and seeking values for the arbitrary constants A, B, decide whether each of the following problems has a unique solution, or many solutions, or no solutions.

(i) $y'' - 3y' + 2y = 0$; $y'(0) = 1$, $y(\ln 2) = 0$

(ii) $y'' - 3y' + 2y = 0$; $y'(0) = 1$, $y(1) = 2$

(iii) $y'' - 3y' + 2y = 0$; $y'(0) = 1$, $y(\ln 2) = 2$

Index